Inte
Care Systems: practical perspectives

Dick Stockford

Longman

Longman Group UK Limited
Longman House, Burnt Mill, Harlow, Essex CM20 2JE

© Longman Group UK Limited, 1988

First published 1988

British Library Cataloguing in Publication Data

Integrating care systems.
   1. Great Britain. local authority.
   I. Stockford, Dick
   352.041

ISBN 0-582-02483-8

Typeset by Quorn Selective Repro Ltd, Loughborough, Leicestershire
Printed and bound in Great Britain by Biddles Ltd, Guildford and King's Lynn.

Dedication

This book is dedicated to my wonderful mother in the hope that if and when she needs care it will have been improved by its publication. Then, it will all have been worthwhile.

Acknowledgement

This book could not have been written without the help and support of my family who have observed with understanding and forbearance the sight of their father and husband furtively scribbling notes and correcting chapters; my colleagues, politicians and officers, both in the County Council and outside it; and the inspiration of the many practitioners and planners who are out there 'doing the business'.

I am particularly grateful to Beverly Beamiss for typing, from illegible notes and to impossible deadlines, to colleagues in the Lincoln Group who have provided me with a constant flow of ideas and inspiration and to my wife, whose insight and perception I value more than she will ever know.

In the end, I am responsible for any faults or inaccuracies that the book contains but I do not believe that its advice, if conscientiously pursued, would ever lead to a diminution of care and could only lead to its improvement.

Disclaimer

Since many of the authors who contributed to this book are practising in statutory authorities, and have written informatively and openly of their experiences, it is important that readers recognise that in no case do the views expressed reflect those of the agencies or departments in which they work, or have worked, but are those of the authors alone.

Contents

Foreword

Now our captains of industry and their lieutenants are aggressive, restless, greedy, urban technocrats, working and playing hard.

The arrivistes are interested in money – to the point of obsession. Pay them one hundred thousand and they'll want two; let them make a million and they'll strive for ten. That's the way we want them. (Stephen Rowlinson, Chief Executive Korn/Ferry International Ltd, letter to *The Times* 3 February 1987)

This book is dedicated to enterprise but not to the enterprise of the Golden Calf. It is an enterprise which demands determination, tact, wit, imagination, understanding and risk. The commitment is not to the pursuit of profit but to the meeting of needs; the values are not self-seeking but altruistic, and the benefits are intangible but socially constructive.

This book is dedicated to all those who have chosen to pursue the unfashionable and often unrewarding goal of working within or between large bureaucracies in search of a better future for their clients and patients. It records the successes (and failures) of some of these entrepreneurs and attempts to chart, for the benefit of their successors, the strengths and pitfalls of their approach.

Introduction

Dick Stockford and Simon Whitehead

The purpose of this book is to lay before the reader as much insight and practical wisdom as can be gleaned from experience. The contributions to this collection are grounded firmly in the real experiences of the authors, who have attempted to guide, nudge and, in some cases, direct the eager practitioner. And to what end?

Simply put, this book represents a response to the challenge presented by care in the community. Can helping agencies combine to respond to human needs in a way that ignores, from the consumer's point of view, agency boundaries? This is a simple challenge, beguilingly self-evident, but one which remains to be aimed for rather than achieved. This book will show that enthusiasm, although a vital ingredient, is not in itself sufficient. The task is uphill, and Sainsbury (1982) neatly encapsulates the problems. 'Effective liaison is difficult to achieve partly because of the structural differences between services, partly because professions hold different perspectives on the care and treatment of people and partly because of difficulties of achieving a mutual understanding of each others' tasks'. To make things worse, not everyone is that enthusiastic: 'A bit like oil and water' was one chief officer's doleful view of housing and social services, 'they won't mix' (Hearnden 1984).

Hearnden (1984) has listed some of the possible causes of disaffection with a cooperating style of working. 'Time consuming, people may only pay lip service to it, it confused functions, it aggravates conflict, it may raise expectations that cannot be fulfilled, it makes for over-elaboration and even through the formalisation of relations, a stifling of innovation; above all it sometimes becomes merely symbolic – coordination for coordination's sake, a vessel making loud sounds because it is empty of achievement'.

This book draws on the experience of planners, practitioners and researchers in order to identify, from each of their perspectives, the issues which they have addressed and to unpick (rather than cut) the very real Gordian Knot that many attempts have produced. To this practical end each chapter concludes with the lessons learned and, wherever possible, some guideposts for the future.

If it is clear that the enterprise is fraught with problems, what distinguishes it from any other hair shirt on the back of the social administrator? To answer this we must turn to the recipient of the social administrators' goods – the customer.

Nobody has an innate human need for a place in an old people's home or a period in a day hospital. Yet so often human needs get defined in terms of existing service provision. Moreover, since services are provided by a number of agencies and organisations, individuals often end up with a range of different services being provided by different people from different departments.

The kind of questions that an individual with simple needs for help and support would ask are: Who will care for me? Will the care help me? Will I have a choice in what happens? In practice, the assessment of need and the provision of services are often made on the basis of what is available to the person undertaking the assessment, and not on the true nature of the need and the appropriate matching of resources. It is often an assessment of someone rather than an assessment for and with someone.

Imagine you are a woman in her nineties living in sheltered housing on the edge of town. Four years ago you had a hip replacement but although still able to get about in your flat you need to use a walking frame. You are mentally quite alert but you forget names and faces, particularly new ones. You might be visited during the course of a week or so by a district nurse (to check the abscess on your leg), a nursing auxiliary (to give you a bath), a home help organiser (to check you still need that home help), a home help (to do the flat), a meals on wheels lady (to bring you a hot meal on Tuesday, Thursday and Friday), a volunteer (to take you to the day centre in town on Wednesday), a social worker (to talk about a home for old people) and a warden (to see that you are all right). There could be others – the general practitioner, the occupational therapist, the lady from the Department of Health and Social Security etc. The chances are that many of these people do not know each other; some won't know the others are visiting; and you, the old lady, do not know why many of them are visiting at all. They all do their own assessments and form their own plans. But how many of them know you and what you want? And do you know (or care) whether they come from the district council housing department, the county council social services department, the district health authority, the Women's Royal Voluntary Service, the Department of Health and Social Security, or Age Concern?

The same is true for people other than the elderly, such as the mother of a child with severe disabilities, a young adult with a mental handicap, the victim of a road traffic accident paralysed from the waist down, or a young man with schizophrenia living in a boarding house. They can all be in contact with a host of services, helpers and professional care workers.

The consequences of services being organised and provided in the ways described are threefold:

1 The customer (or service user) may get a service but there is no guarantee it will meet their needs.
2 It is unlikely that the resources committed will be being used efficiently or as effectively as possible.
3 It is unlikely that the planning and development of new services will be informed by a process that identifies desired service outcomes to meet known needs.

These issues are the basis for the case for integrating care systems in both development and implementation. Human services exist to meet the care needs of individuals: why else do they exist? Moreover, individuals do not see each separate need they have in isolation: they experience them as whole people, with a complex interaction of biological, psychological, sociological and spiritual variables. A service received for one need may affect either a different need, or another service being received for another need. At the individual level, needs and services should be looked at together, so that service responses are relevant, programmed, complementary and consistent. They will then be based on what people want and need, are are more likely to be economic, efficient and effective.

In many ways it sounds self-evident, and yet in practice and in planning it is far from simple. The multiplicity of sources of care, ranging from the most informal provided by spouses and families to the most structured provided by major institutions, like hospitals, ensure that the process is complex, confusing and frequently avoided. The business of integration, of collaboration, of joint planning has become an industry of its own: with multidisciplinary teams, joint care planning teams, joint consultative committees, joint development officers and a whole plethora of coordinators. That is because of the importance attached to the issues – both in terms of the services offered and in terms of their value for money. Unless individuals and their needs are at the heart of the process, however, the integration will be over-structured, mechanistic and un-helpful.

If that is why integrating care systems is of relevance then what are the difficulties? What needs to be done? How is it being tackled and by whom?

Finding the common ground: value systems

Agencies, organisations and professions have their own historical contexts and legislative bases and are inevitably at different stages of development to each other. They operate with different cultures, expectations, language, protocol and structures. Their account-abilities vary. It is therefore hardly surprising that they often find it difficult to talk to each other: the opportunities for misunderstanding, miscommunication and frustration are endless.

There needs to be a common factor in and between all those involved. The one thing that all should have in common is the object of their endeavours – that is the client/patient/customer. Starting with the person who is in need of assistance cuts through all the constraints and factors in the operating environment. If agreement cannot be reached about who is the object of concern and why, then integration becomes meaningless. Identifying who (at least in the most general sense) is easy: it may be people who are elderly or people with a mental handicap. But identifying more specifically who and why is not so easy, and can sometimes be painful – because this is about values and what we think about people: the value that is (or is not) attributed to people, the value that is (or is not) attributed to people who are often not always quite like other people; people who may be unattractive, even disfigured; who may be dying; or who may not be successful in terms of the way success is normally defined (economic, physical prowess, material wealth, academic achieve-ment, etc).

Those involved in the care of others, either in a personal capacity or in a professional capacity as a practitioner, manager or planner, presumably consider it a worthwhile endeavour. Otherwise why are they doing it, or should they be doing it?

Understanding and making clear statements about basic human values then become the starting point. The difficulty is that often these statements are easily made and agreed to without due thought being given to the extent of the commitment to them. This can be seen in the way human services in practice so often contradict or ignore the very values people are so willing to subscribe to, and in such simple and basic ways – like agreeing about the importance of such things as the right of old people to dignity and privacy, and then finding that toilets in old people's homes frequently have no locks and are often left open whilst in use by an elderly person. Agreement about values cannot be seen as complete unless such commitment is challenged, acknowledged, and clearer service principles based on the values are identified. In this context it is helpful to examine what happens to specific individuals in practice as a way of challenging real allegiance to overall value statements.

Service principles take further the implications of values in practice; they begin to elaborate the criteria against which services can be assessed in relation to these basic values. They enable the painful process of identifying how near or far people really stand in relation to these values. An example of the use of such a statement of values and service principles is shown below in an extract from a joint strategic framework developed by a number of agencies concerned with mental health services in one area[1].

Being flexible: coping with bureaucracy

Many of the services offering care to people are provided by large bureaucratic organisations. That is to say they are provided by agencies whose size is such that labour has to be divided and a hierarchical system of authority is required. Because of their size, their hierarchies and the rules and procedures that are necessary to make them function in a controlled and controllable way, they inevitably become conservative: they depend on stability and do not adapt easily to change. They become rigid, centralised and formal structures.

Yet they are dealing with people devalued and disadvantaged in a society where attitudes, politics, demography, economics and technology are causing constant change: an unstable environment. To meet this challenge services need to adapt themselves quickly in responding to changing needs.

In large, centralised, mechanistic organisations this is very difficult. Communication becomes a major problem: too much interconnection is required. Managers and practitioners are required to communicate with too many other people, units, sections and organisations before action can be taken. Deliberation proliferates, at a high cost: how often is it said 'We need a working party' or 'A sub-group has been set up'? There follows an over-concentration on procedure rather than process. Decision-making becomes uncertain: it is not clear how decisions are made, or by whom, or who influences them. In this environment the possibilities for the abuse of power grow as people take 'political' positions and vested interests are established; there is a lack of trust. Ideas and projects fizzle out through the sheer complexity and complications of getting anything done or agreed. There is a consequent loss of morale.

If it is difficult within just one of these bureaucracies, it is certainly going to be more difficult between two, let alone three or more. So to increase the chances of success the effect of bureaucracy needs to be minimised. This requires the identification of key people in the joint planning process, understanding between them about the processes and issues within their respective organisations, and agreement about value systems. If this can be achieved, over-formalised joint planning systems can be avoided and the numbers of people involved can be kept small. By involving those with the power (informal or otherwise) to make decisions and implement them; by concentrating on trust between the participants, excessive rules and procedures can be avoided.

Providing integrated care based on the needs of individuals requires a high degree of flexibility in the way services are planned, organised and managed. Any service that is prescribed, proceduralised and institutionalised (in the sense that it is closed, routine and uniform) will not adapt to individual or changing needs. As soon as services become large, widespread and complex to manage, bureaucracy creeps in. Keeping them as small and autonomous as possible helps retain their adaptability and relevance to customer need.

Getting beyond professional boundaries

Other than the personal and informal care from relatives and friends, caring has gradually been professionalised. That is, those groups involved in the caring process have defined in their own special jargon the problems they think have been presented to them; and have subsequently prescribed the solutions they think should be applied to these problems. They have decided they know best; special training courses have been established; bodies of knowledge in special language have been developed; special associations have been founded to further the cause of particular professions, with selective rules of entry.

Despite this process developing over this century, it is sometimes difficult to identify exactly what progress has been made for some groups of disadvantaged people. Indeed, it can be argued that the introduction of a professional approach in some areas of caring has actually led to the exclusion of people from services on the grounds that their needs fall outside the specialist remit of that particular service: the disabled man sent home from a hostel for the physically handicapped because he is too handicapped; the young person with severe learning difficulties banned from the training centre and left at home with her parents because she is too difficult.

If the purpose of integrating care systems is to provide services based on a holistic approach to helping people, then the negative aspects and narrow boundaries of professionalism need to be reduced and broken down. The professional imperialism demonstrated in arguments and border wars between social workers and community psychiatric nurses, between physiotherapists and occupational therapists, between clinical psychologists and psychiatrists, can only be counter-productive.

Again, it is a matter of going beyond the concern that professionals have about what they do or do not do for people; and looking instead at the specific needs of the individual in question, agreeing with them what is required, and identifying and agreeing who has the skills and resources to provide it. The strength of successful multidisciplinary teams is usually seen in the appropriate matching of needs and resources, irrespective of which professional group the participants happen to belong to. Teams that spend a good deal of time examining the respective roles and responsibilities of different team members are likely to obscure the identification of who the client actually is, his needs and wants, and how best he might be helped.

Getting closer to the customer: devolving

This has been the slogan for some time in certain industrial and commercial concerns, and is now at the centre of the latest management cult[2]. In more general terms it refers to the issues already discussed: finding out what the customer wants and needs and seeking to supply it. But this is affected, particularly in relation to human services, by the accessibility of the services, both physically and psychologically and by the way they involve the customer and are accountable to them. The trend in social services departments is increasingly expressed in terms of decentralisation and going local. The same move towards patch-based, integrated local services is suggested in the Cumberlege Report on the future of community nursing. In the field of joint planning similar developments can be seen in the concept of locality planning that originated in the Exeter Health Authority area: on the basis that planning for a community should be based on a community – and a community is not 300,000 people, nor even 100,000 people. Local planning involves local people with local knowledge of local need: service strategies to meet need are locally derived and supported. Public, volunteer and individual involvement in assessment, care and its planning is made easier and more relevant. The need for complex coordination mechanisms is reduced and the best use of local resources is encouraged.

Sadly, it is not as straightforward as it sounds. The evidence from the first major decentralisation in a social services department (*Whose Welfare*, S. Croft and P. Beresford) suggests that clients felt no nearer the service, nor did they experience the service as more relevant or responsive to their needs. The difficulty is twofold: first that the strictures of bureaucracy, of the tendency to ritualise responses into systems that become ends in themselves, must first be overcome. And second that accountability needs to be clarified and possibly changed. Social services departments are run by elected members of the county or borough council, through a social services committee. They are accountable to the electorate for services provided and so quite rightly will expect the managers and practitioners in the department to be accountable to them. But where does this leave the individual old person or young adult with a mental handicap? Clients of social services departments are usually members of minority groups held in low esteem by their communities and society at large. Should not the home help or social worker be accountable to them? How else can the service they receive be based on their needs? Is the only way to achieve this direct accountability through a direct contractual relationship between client and service provider, ie through income maintenance and the privatisation of services?

Freeing people to act: delegation

Staff constrained by rules, procedures and an over-concern for role will not be able to respond flexibly to the people they are trying to help. Lack of freedom to do what may be obvious will make the help irrelevant to the client, and can only result in an inefficient and ineffective use of resources. Of course staff need to be managed, supervised and supported; but they also need to feel trusted, to be credible in the eyes of their client; and if they are going to collaborate in a flexible way with staff from other agencies and organisations, they need the freedom to use their discretion and act in ways that seem appropriate without recourse to other people or systems of authority.

Indeed, decentralising services as discussed earlier is dependent for effective working on a high degree of delegation. If an organisation is over-controlled and is trying to decentralise, hierarchy will proliferate and services will become bound by all the negative aspects of bureaucracy. If this is difficult to achieve in one agency (reducing controls, delegating authority, giving staff the freedom to respond flexibly to people's needs and demands) where accountability is not always clear, the problems are clearly exacerbated when staff from different professions and agencies are working together in multidisciplinary settings or joint planning forums.

The essence of delegation is trust: without it there can be none. It means living with the ambiguity of the need for control on the one hand and trust on the other. If you seek to control, how can you be said to trust? But a balance can be achieved: ultimately control can spring from firmly held trust. How can this develop?

1 Trust is about values, first and foremost; it was described earlier how joint working at any level is ultimately dependent on a common understanding about the answer to the question 'why?'. Agreement between people about attitudes and ideologies is an essential prerequisite to effective joint working and to effective delegation.

2 Responsibility needs to be jointly defined by manager and subordinate; this means agreeing about overall objectives based on a similarly agreed set of desired outcomes.

3 The manager should ideally appoint the staff for whom he or she is responsible. Trust is based to a large extent on less tangible and personal factors, like intuition, a meeting of minds and a mutual respect, which are more likely to occur if individuals are choosing to work with each other.

4 Trust needs to be earned and sensitively maintained. Trust is essentially about risk; risks that come off earn trust; risks that fail can, if not carefully, immediately and jointly worked at, destroy trust rapidly. Once destroyed, trust is very difficult to revive.

If all these things happen and have positive outcomes, then the essential trust will exist, and will become the control itself; and delegation can work. But as with anything joint, it is difficult enough to achieve within one agency or organisation; when staff are working in multidisciplinary teams at practitioner or planning levels, then delegation is not just to one person or part of one organisation, but to people working in other agencies taking part in the joint endeavour. An effective joint team must have the combined and collective delegated authority of all its constituent bodies. This implies delegating the authority of one agency to staff working in another. Trust is the only successful vehicle if agreed joint action is required – trust from constituent bodies to their staff, and then between staff of the constituent bodies at all levels.

If this is our aim this book represents the extent we fall short of it, or, more optimistically, how close we come to it.

The balance between formal planning systems and the need of individuals within it is brought into sharp focus by Gerald Wistow and Peter Whittingham writing of their experiences during and following research on the Joint Approach to Social Policy (Jasp). Their rediscovery of 'organisational rationality', which attempts to understand not just the needs of customers but also of the planners and practitioners concerned with providing service, leads them to criticise the 'architectural' approach to planning adopted by central government. Putting into practice the findings of his research caused

Whittingham to surmise that the days of formal planning machinery are numbered.

Surveying the literature associated with coordination between statutory and voluntary organisations, Leat (1983) concluded that her review 'highlights just how little systematic evidence there is on the history, nature and process of such relationships'. Nick Miller has brought the available literature up to date and views it from a research practitioner point of view; he has drawn out those aspects of the relationship which require both further consideration and more determined action by statutory agencies bent on developing a joint service relationship.

But Gerald Wistow has tried to set the local developments into a national policy context which demonstrates the genesis of many of the problems with which practitioners locally have to deal. At the root there lies the aspirations of politicians. These aspirations are shown to coalesce behind the care in the community approach to service problems, with very different motivations: the benefit of efficiency and economy appealing to one, a more localised form of management to another and a responsive community based service to another. These differing aspirations are not in themselves unusual, but added to the different, and sometimes competing, objectives of health, social services, housing departments and voluntary organisations, set the scene for a dramatic set of interactions.

These differences were so keenly felt amongst parents of mentally handicapped children in one local authority that they decided, in the words of the chairman of their voluntary organisation, to 'go it alone'. These parents felt annoyed to the point of separate development, although their struggle to improve services, as chronicled by Robert Nisbet, shows the importance of conflict in bringing about changes in attitudes needed to cooperate in and provide services which were used previously 'as a last resort'. There are a great number of lessons to be learned, in a practical way, about the relationship between professionals and parents, but it is most regrettable if the frustrations and problems associated with caring for handicapped children have to boil over into distrust of all professionals before such change can take place. The need to ensure that the often rigid boundaries between organisations are made permeable by the work of the entrepreneur is detailed clearly in the work of Malcolm Cooper and Michael White, writing respectively about housing services and the transfer of resources. A clear vision of the need to develop joint housing services for elderly people and to ensure that care is linked closely and permanently to its provision is an obvious strength of Cooper's entrepreneurial style. These skills are even more sharply etched in the negotiations that Cooper describes between district council, county council, housing association, housing corporation and the Department of the Environment, in order to ensure that each of the elements of the scheme could be funded and the requirement for joint care understood by the funding bodies.

A different vision, but one held equally firmly, is demonstrated in White's comparison of negotiations between a local authority social services department and two different health authorities to develop services for mentally handicapped people leaving hospitals on a transferred funding basis. The learning experience from one negotiation was put to good use in the subsequent (and successful) negotiations with the other health authority. The case study demonstrates very clearly the interaction between the formal and informal system of negotiations and the role that serendipity can play in planning.

A constant call from those involved in the development of integrated systems, be they entrepreneurs or bureaucrats, is the request for more information on the progress of schemes and more evaluation against which to judge the success or otherwise of the enterprise. David Symes and Rob Ballantyne, writing from a health service perspective, identify the shortfalls and suggest some ways of closing 'the information gap'. They do so aware of the fact that information is neither neutral nor a simple matter of providing more information to more managers. They recognise that the provision of information itself is a challenge to managers who often, in joint negotiations, feel exposed, and identify clearly the need to target particular pieces of information to particular managers in order to maximise effect. But their plea for a more rigorous assessment of service provision will be echoed by many service providers; Judy Renshaw and Corinne Thomason have answered some of these requests but generate more still. Their wide ranging review of 28 care in the community projects developed over the past three years reinforces the need both for a clear philosophical agreement between agencies and, underpinning this, clear information concerning outcomes. There can be little doubt that if the days of the formal planning system are numbered, the days of the information scientist will be long.

References

Sainsbury, E (1982) in *Linking Health Care and Social Services: Internation Perspectives*, Hokenstad, M C and Ritvo R A (eds), London, Sage.

Hearnden, D (1984) *Co-ordinating Housing and Social Services: From Good Intentions to Good Practice*, London Centre for Policy on Ageing.

Leat, D (1983) 'Working Together: Statutory/Voluntary Relationships in Collaboration and Conflict' in *Working with Others: Research Highlights 7*, Lishman, J (ed), Aberdeen, University of Aberdeen, Department of Social Work.

Notes

1   Values and principles: many people with mental health problems lose, forfeit or are deprived of their value and dignity; the causes range from problems within an individual or problems in an individual's relationships with other people, to problems in the wider community. The result is that people are unable to use approved ways or opportunities to regain their value, self-respect and ability to accept responsibility; this experience leads them to use ways that are not approved or services that treat them as second-class citizens. They become further deprived and separated from ordinary life opportunity. It is the task of mental health services to break this vicious circle for individuals and families, by helping them to regain their sense of worth, self-respect, and ability to contribute to society.

This approach is firmly based on two primary values:

-   every individual should have opportunities to pursue a normal pattern of life in the community, irrespective of origin, status, sex, age, creed or contribution to society.
-   people have rights to self-determination and choice, responsibilities, value and dignity and these should be respected at all times.

Services which aim to restore, enhance or sustain the value and dignity of individual people should:

-   be based on an understanding of what individuals want and need, and what most people approve and prefer, rather than what is available.
-   be as local as possible to the individual's needs and wishes.
-   support, not supplant, existing relationships and social networks.
-   be integrated and comprehensive so that the needs of people are met across a wide area of their lives in coordinated and continuous ways.
-   provide shelter based on ordinary domestic arrangements that allows the continuation of individual life styles.
-   seek to integrate individuals back into the community; specialist or segregated facilities should be avoided except when a service is not available or not appropriately provided in an ordinary setting.
-   involve individuals, and where appropriate their families, in planning for their needs to be met.
-   seek to minimise dependence on statutory services.
-   be provided on an equitable basis in the overall catchment area.

The importance of these statements is not that they are instantly achievable but that they set the ultimate goals, and provide an essential yardstick in measuring how effective a service is. The choice of which service options to pursue should thus always be based on the ones most in tune with the principles and values that are also achievable.

2   See for example *In Search of Excellence*, T. Peters and R. H. Waterman, and *A Passion for Excellence*, T. Peters and N. Austin.

1a The joint planning maze

Brian Gale, Gill Garton and Andrew Webster

Why bother with joint planning? We all know how much time everyone wastes talking about plans while services moulder, and anyway the whole system is irrational. Implicitly most people think their own agency should control the whole of care in the community. Most people don't know who controls what in any case! Equally nearly all workers involved in community care are motivated by goodwill and a wish to help their clients despite difficult circumstances and bizarre organisational arrangements. Joint planning, for us, is about working our way round and through these bureaucratic mazes so that we can all make the best use of one anothers' talents, ideas and resources. That way all our clients should benefit.

The letters page of your local paper probably reveals the struggle involved in changing the style of care we offer the most disabled people in society. The nursing homes mushrooming in southern England show how difficult it is for the public sector to cope with the growing numbers of very old people. The scale of services called for and the responsibility for delivering them is changing quickly. All the more reason for those taking on new roles and those losing old ones to work in partnership rather than rivalry. Planning services together, and changing the way we plan them, is a vital part of that process.

This chapter is about developing joint planning in a shire county. In most areas some kind of joint working has evolved, and everywhere has a statutory framework for joint planning. In Cambridgeshire we are moving from an ad hoc approach to allocating joint finance and checking out each others approaches towards a more comprehensive structure which underpins common policies for achieving care in the community. This presentation of our efforts focuses on the practitioner's experience of joint planning and uses the questions you would ask to illuminate features of the work undertaken in the county.

The material is organised into three sections. The first introduces you to the joint planning team, assesses its potential, examines your role and looks at how to get the most effective groups of people working together for agreed goals. The second section considers how to get changes in practice or new services going as a result of joint planning. It concentrates on resource allocation and making managers take notice of what joint planning teams say and do. Thirdly we look at how the methods we adopted go beyond the marginal matters of joint finance and exchanging information and start building common programmes, procedures and practices. We describe induction, training and evaluation and set out a model for joint statements of intent.

Where am I?

On a fraught Monday morning the memo arrives telling you that you have been selected to represent the department on the joint planning team for 'good things'. You put it on one side until half an hour before the meeting, get lost in the hospital and arrive ten minutes late. What next? More often than not this is the practitioners' introduction to joint planning. Given this sort of start you are likely to ask these sort of questions.

Who are all these people?

You may recognise one or two friendly faces, but many of them are likely to be strangers. On being introduced you would discover that they represent several agencies and professions all concerned with the same subject – if not you may still be lost!

What is the purpose of the group?

Depending on who you speak to you will get a different answer. Some will want to discuss a current operational problem, others to swap stories and some may be interested in planning services.

What contribution can I make?

It's quite likely that you will be uncertain as to whether your role is as a specialist on operational matters or as a planner for new services. If the latter is the case then you will want guidance on about how far you represent your department, how far you can commit your management, whether you have access to your agency's resources.

Who is going to take any notice of the group?

If the group does make a recommendation someone will have to arrange for its implementation. Advice will need to be channelled to decision makers (management and/or politicians) in the appropriate authority. There should be a system by which they respond to the team's work.

We found that such questions frequently concerned participants in joint planning groups in Cambridgeshire. People were unsure about the purpose of the group, their role in it and its ability to influence decisions and get things done. This lead to frustration and disillusionment.

We tackled these problems on four fronts:

Terms of reference

It is essential to have a clearly defined purpose which is recognised and agreed by the participating authorities and understood by their representatives. In Cambridgeshire it was agreed to have a joint development team for each client group with these terms of reference:

1. On the basis of the policies of the constituent agencies (including those in the joint statement of intent), to prepare integrated care plans for the total client group and make recommendations to constituent agencies and the joint consultative committee.
2. To monitor and support arrangements for the coordination of services provided by constituent agencies.
3. To assess proposals, plans and operational problems referred by constituent agencies and to provide advice.

To translate this statement into action joint development teams are encouraged to develop detailed work programmes, based on an agreed set of objectives, which are monitored and reviewed every six months.

Membership

If the group is going to fulfill its terms of reference it is important that it has the appropriate membership both in terms of its size (too small and it's not representative, too large and it becomes cumbersome) and in terms of ability to make commitments. In Cambridgeshire the following criteria for membership were agreed:

1. Membership should be at a level which allows teams to function most effectively. A maximum of nine members is suggested.
2. Team members should be in a position to represent their own agencies' policies to carry forward jointly developed proposals within

their agencies and to give preliminary commitment on behalf of their sponsoring organisations.

3　Recognising the constraints of time, joint development team members will need to be in a position to take a broad overview rather than bring specialist input to the team (the specialist input will be required for sub-groups). One team member should serve on the joint coordinating group.

4　The convenors of joint development teams should be agreed jointly by the constituent agencies and reviewed annually.

Implicit in this guidance was the need for members to be of sufficient seniority in their organisation, a requirement to concentrate on the general development of services rather than getting bogged down in detail which could be delegated to sub-groups and the need for the team to establish a link with management and the decision making processes of the participating agencies. In practice this means members are service managers, unit general managers, medical consultants, area social services directors, senior housing and education officers and influential members of voluntary organisations.

TABLE 1a.1　A joint scheme's path through the planners' maze

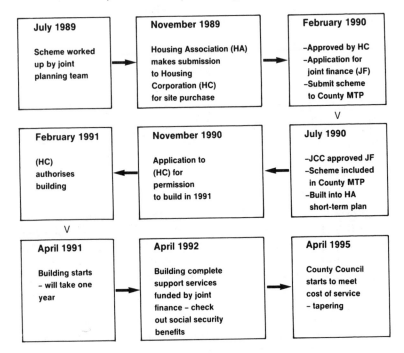

Links between teams and management

Having got the right people we then had to ensure that there was a system for allocating tasks and guiding their work towards political priorities. In Cambridgeshire we recognised the need for co-ordination across client groups and between joint planning teams and the joint consultative committee. To achieve this it was agreed that the work of joint development teams would be overseen by a group of senior managers (District General Managers, Directors of Housing, Assistant Director of Social Services, Area Education Officer, District Medical Officer and Secretary of Council of Voluntary Service) from participating agencies, called the joint coordinating group. Its role was to focus effort on joint planning priorities and deal with matters affecting more than one client group. It also oversees the implementation of agreed recommendations by channelling them to the relevant operational and financial managers.

Information and support

For anybody to work effectively within the system they need to know how it works, and what is expected of them. Initially Cambridgeshire County Council briefed its own representatives separately on processes and priorities. Subsequently this was extended to joint briefings of planning teams on a wide range of subjects relevant to their work. Some information was circulated in briefing notes, but more emphasis was placed on presentations to groups of members or team meetings.

One off briefings are useful but to work well the system needed more continuous support. This applies both to servicing the joint planning teams – agenda, minutes etc – and also to technical advice and planning expertise. The need for such support is especially apparent when one comes to look at financial planning. This involves harnessing the resources of health services and social services planning staff, corporate research and policy staff and keeping on good terms with the accountants.

The heart of the maze: funding your plans

For most groups the crucial question was how to get resources for new proposals. This opens up the complexities of planning and managing joint services. How much they affect the programmes of participating agencies is the basic measure of the effectiveness of joint planning teams. So a key task was to ensure that their proposals were suitably framed and geared to the resource allocation mechanisms of the main agencies involved. To achieve this you will need an understanding of how participating agencies allocate funds between competing needs. This is not easy! Each agency operates according to its own rules, procedures and timetable within different political frameworks. A simple presentation of the various systems is often a revelation to senior managers let alone to practitioners.

Nothing is more frustrating for a team than to see a well thought out proposal fail because it was submitted at the wrong time through the wrong channels because nobody knew how the system worked. Cambridgeshire's files contain some very good ideas which have been delayed (perhaps forever) because they missed the submission dates in one or other agencies' planning cycle. Effective joint planning needs to guide good ideas over the hurdles implicit in systems where money is scarce, as well as communicate basic information.

Existing strategies and programmes

For a newcomer to joint planning, the strategic plans and forward programmes of the authorities involved would seem a useful starting point. It is probably true that bids for resources which fall within the priorities set out in the existing strategies will do better than ones which don't – for instance there would be little prospect of securing funds for a new hostel for 25 mentally handicapped people now in the local hospital if everyone is agreed that it is best to accommodate all the ex-patients in ordinary houses.

However, the combined strategic plans for Cambridgeshire weigh about 30 lbs and several years' deadlines would have passed by the time you'd read them all. It makes sense to get hold of a summary of the plans or to ask to be briefed on the important points for the area you are working in. One of the first tasks we tackled in Cambridgeshire was drawing up summaries of each District Health Authorities' Strategic Plans – itemising proposals by client group and for each year. At the same time Social Services put together Position Statements on their services for each client group.

Changing forward programmes: how agencies get and allocate money

The Local Authorities obtain resources from three main sources. Firstly from the government mainly through the rate support grant but also grants for specific purposes. Secondly through the rates. Thirdly from income generated by charging for services (eg rent) or from sales of assets (eg council houses). The annual budgets are prepared in the period from December to about March when expenditure and the rate level is agreed by the Council. In preparing the budget the Council will need to consider the level of service it wishes to provide, the level of grant from the government and the desired level of rates.

In the case of Cambridgeshire County Council the level of expenditure is determined by its three year financial plan known as the Medium Term Plan (MTP) which provides a framework for deciding priorities and allocating money. To obtain additional money for services all departments are required to submit their proposals for approval in the Medium Term Plan. In most cases new money is only available in year three of the plan and thus there is a fairly long wait between submitting the scheme and getting the money to implement it. For example a scheme submitted in January 1988 will not obtain funding until April 1991.

Money for the District Councils' Housing Programmes is allocated through the Housing Investment Programme (HIP) which is submitted for approval to the Department of Environment each July. The HIP is a two year plan and finance for major new schemes is usually not available until the second year.

Housing Associations obtain revenue from rents, housing sales and a grant from the Housing Corporation. Each year the Housing Association submits its programme to the Housing Corporation for approval. The approval for schemes is in two stages. The Corporation will initially approve expenditure to purchase the site in the next financial year. Following this, the Housing Association will need to make a further bid the next year for approval to build on the site. Sometimes there is a frustrating delay of more than a year between the two stages and there can be a considerable timelag between getting initial authorisation and completion.

District Health Authorities get annual allocations from Regional Health Authorities according to a formula based on norms and how much of a service they provide for other districts. Exact allocations are in practice negotiable – if your team puts up a scheme which is accepted as a regional priority, special funds can often be found. Districts don't know exactly what they will get until almost the start of that financial year – so they plan on assumptions. Their plans are set out in two year Short Term Programmes. The first year is what the Authority expects to do next year, and the second year suggests plans for the following one. These plans have to conform to regional and national guidelines – for instance all Districts must plan services for drug users. They should also promote the aims set out in Strategic Plans. The Plan must also include capital expenditure and 'cost improvements'.

Timetables

Each agency operates its own planning calender which sets out dates for the submission of proposals and the selection of successful schemes. A crucial date in this timetable is the deadline for submitting schemes to the funding authorities. The key task therefore is to look at the different planning timetables of some of the main agencies concerned.

In Cambridgeshire the County Council's departments will start assembling bids for inclusion in its MTP from about October onwards for submission to their committee in March.

District Councils in shire counties will be preparing their budgets for the next financial year from about October onwards and there could be scope for incorporating small levels of housing expenditure for high priority schemes providing they are submitted by this date. For larger amounts of expenditure proposals need to be included in the Housing Investment Programme and put forward by about May in time for submission of the final document to the Department of the Environment in July.

Housing Associations are required to present their plans for expenditure to the Housing Corporation in November and will need to be aware of proposals by about July.

District Health Authority Short Term Programmes are generally prepared in the summer for the following year. In practice specific proposals should be ready for inclusion by June.

Integrating the timetables

To stand any chance of obtaining funding for your scheme it is important to make submission to the appropriate agency by the deadline. Some agencies already work to a fairly long timetable and a late submission can only add to the frustration of a practitioner wishing to see something get off the ground immediately. Some of the planning systems take three to four years to get a scheme off the ground – be patient! – the results will be worth it. If more than one agency is involved in financing the scheme then it is crucial that the project is prepared in time for the earliest deadline.

It is too much to expect a person to remember the deadlines of all the organisations involved in joint planning. A simple table was therefore produced which listed the deadline dates for submitting schemes for any particular implementation year.

TABLE 1a.2   Deadline dates for submitting schemes

Implementation YEAR	Deadline for submission of schemes				
	Health Authority	Joint Finance	County Council	District Council	Housing Association
1990/1	July 89	Feb 89	Jan 87	May 89	Nov 89
1991/2	July 90	Feb 90	Jan 88	May 90	Nov 89
1992/3	July 91	Feb 91	Jan 89	May 90	Nov 89

Table 1a.2 shows, for example, that if the Health Authority and County Council were to jointly finance a scheme for implementation in 1991/2 then it would need to be submitted to the County Council by January 1988 even although the Health Authority would not need to be notified of the proposal until July 1989.

Another complexity to jointly funded schemes is that capital expenditure and revenue expenditure is required at different times. For example, a District Council may finance the capital cost of building a group home with the County Council agreeing to provide the support services (the revenue expenditure). There is obviously a time lag between the start of construction and the need for the support services of at least a year. This will influence the timing of your bids.

Picking the winners

Joint planning teams shouldn't waste time working on schemes that stand little chance of approval. Because of uncertainty and the different ways agencies operate it is difficult to predict precisely which initiatives are likely to be adopted. Nonetheless, there should be information available which can guide the team in deciding which proposals to put forward at any given time. This information will include: an indication of the amount of money available, criteria used by each agency to judge the merits of schemes, and guidance on how a scheme should be presented.

In Cambridgeshire guidelines are issued annually to all joint planning teams covering timetable, resource availability and selection criteria. They are also given regular updates on the current status of the Health Authorities' and County Council's plans. Housing representatives on the teams are also expected to brief other members.

Joint finance

The difficulty of timetabling and picking winners was clearly illustrated by the operation of the joint finance programme. The system operated in a vacuum with no guidance on priorities, programming or consideration of how they would fit in with the financial systems of participating organisations. Schemes were considered on a first come first served basis and often failed to obtain approval because the agency concerned was unable to make provision for picking up the tapering. Many planning teams felt disillusioned after spending many hours preparing proposals which were rejected.

To rectify this guidelines were issued which established clear priorities and a two stage timetable for the joint consultative committee (JCC) to recommend schemes. Stage one involved inviting joint development teams to put up outline ideas roughly 13 months before intended start date (assumed to be April 1 of following year). The JCC considers these outlines and shortlists the best for further preparatory work. In stage two the detailed proposals are examined by the JCC at least six months before the intended start date and a final programme is then agreed. Joint initiation and appraisal of schemes moves joint planning on from crude fair shares to promoting agreed priorities.

Transfers of resources and bridging arrangements

When teams are serious about community care joint finance will, of course, never be sufficient to fund major programmes. For those teams need to look to base budgets, transfers of resources and bridging funding. So don't get hooked on small doses of new money, the important resources are already being spent on the wrong things. The transfer and bridging arrangements set out in DHSS Circular HC83(6) are there to get money out of institutions into the community – joint finance is just a sweetener!

In Cambridgeshire we are briefing all joint development teams on the arrangements for transfers of resources and the Regional Health Authority's approach to bridging funds. They are required to consider transfer schemes at the same time as they work up joint finance schemes so that they can be included in Short Term Programmes and the County's forward plans. Joint development teams are expected to examine the use of all resources in their client group not just additional funds available at the margins.

Drawing a map

A number of factors seemed essential if a durable and coherent joint planning system was going to be constructed in the county. These were: clear roles and responsibilities for participants in joint planning teams, clear remits for teams, a widely understood structure for allocating resources and determining policy, good information for participants, shared goals, common working procedures, good feedback and evaluation, and a bit of luck.

In Cambridgeshire we adopted a single vehicle to bring these characteristics to our joint planning arrangements. We called it a joint statement of intent. The statements comprise joint objectives, agenda plans and work programmes for joint planning teams and a manual of joint planning procedures.

This is an attempt to move beyond our existing Health plans, Housing plans and Social Services plans by creating a common strategy for community care. Of course this strategy can't replace the systems which sovereign authorities use to allocate their resources. The joint statement of intent expresses their shared commitment to developing high quality community care, with effective contributions from all partners and as such underpins their individual programmes. Increasingly the voluntary sector is an influential partner in this process.

How was the statement put together?

The starting point was the existing strategies of the agencies involved. The main objectives in these plans provided a basis for joint development teams to start defining common objectives. All the joint development teams have considered and agreed service objectives for their client group. They have also advised on operational topics like joint working practices, social security benefits and relations with voluntary organisations, which cover all client groups.

What are the objectives for?

Primarily they will provide a basis for planning the work of the joint development teams and assessing progress. Each joint development team has set out an agenda plan based on the shared objectives which sets timetables for the work of the team with target dates for reporting and implementation. Secondly they give senior managers a set of goals to use in assessing the work of joint planning teams, for checking their own effectiveness in building up community care services and to help them organise appropriate briefing and support to their representatives. Thirdly, they will constitute a public commitment to joint working by all the agencies involved in community care, and give political direction to joint planning. The joint objectives are now included in Social Services Service Plan and the revised Strategy Document of Cambridge Health Authority.

Joint procedures

The joint statement of intent is about ways of working together as well as about the overall purpose of joint planning. The procedures summarise the roles of agencies involved in joint working and how the joint groups operate. It also sets out common systems for such things as allocating and evaluating joint finance proposals, applying for bridging funds, drawing up joint management agreements, developing joint training programmes and registering private and voluntary homes. The procedures are advisory notes, based on experience with past problems and offer a checklist of points that joint development teams need to consider when making plans for new services. They will be updated as new problems are encountered and as joint working evolves into new fields.

Coping with change

Community care is developing quickly and ideas about good practice, funding arrangements and planning opportunities change rapidly. To keep up the objectives will be reviewed briefly about once a year, and the agenda plans every six months. From time to time more far reaching reviews are necessary – looking at the memberships and working style of joint planning teams.

After four years, the structures and culture of joint planning in Cambridgeshire are well established. We are now reducing the size of formal teams, using them to coordinate ad hoc project groups. The old 'one rep from each profession' rule of group formation is being overtaken by systems which draw more selectively and more effectively on expertise. Representation is more senior and closer to decision makers. Joint planning team members are expected to make commitments which will stick.

Linking plans to power

The extra effort and expense involved in strengthening representation on joint planning teams is only justifiable if they can get through to the bodies which make decisions and affect outcomes. The joint coordinating group should communicate recommendations to the Committees of all the Authorities and can ensure that the joint consultative committee has better things to do than rubber stamp the joint finance programme stitched up by the officers. Systematic monitoring and evaluation of each scheme and of the whole joint planning process is essential.

Lessons learned and signposts

It would need another book to describe some of the pleasing successes and embarrassing failures in Cambridgeshire's experiences of joint planning – we still get the uneasy feeling that we've been through it all before. We have merely pulled together some themes which emerge from the chaos of keeping the show going.

Cambridgeshire will be different from many other areas (it's flatter for a start). Not all of you will have four Health Districts and Six District Councils to deal with. Generally speaking Cambridgeshire has invested a great deal in building up a secure system – with high levels of staff support and catholic interests. There is a joint planning team for everything from AIDS to alarm systems. This gives us a framework for major organisational changes like localisation and ways of routinely presenting joint information to bodies like the Health Advisory Service, the Audit Commission and the Social Services Inspectorate. Inevitably issues fall between teams, or cut across responsibilities and some tensions can only be resolved by ad hoc interventions. Equally, we might be further on in service terms if we had concentrated on one project to the exclusion of all others, as some other areas have done with striking results.

Overall the main messages are:

– joint planning teams are only a good idea if everyone knows why they exist and what they should be doing and when.
– the key performance measure is the impact joint planning makes on resource allocation – so access to the systems which do this is crucial.
– there must be commitment at all levels from practitioners through to members – and straightforward links between them.
– a joint planning system needs informers, trainers, messengers and police to keep the wheels turning.
– a joint commitment to shared aims, accepted roles and agreed work programmes is a sound basis for making joint planning central to all agencies' lives.
– outcomes need to be monitored so that success can be objectively tested.

1b Policy and research into practice

Gerald Wistow and Peter Whittingham

The policy context and the need for collaboration

The current administrative framework for the health and personal social services dates from the simultaneous reorganisations of the NHS and local government which came into effect in 1974. The distribution of functions between the reorganised services was based on a single fundamental principle: that their responsibilities should be demarcated according to the skills of providers rather than the needs of the individuals they served.[1] The major consequence to flow from the application of this principle was the transfer of community health services from local government to new area health authorities, where they were managed alongside hospital services. Thus the 1974 reorganisations completed the administrative divorce of health and social care services, a process initiated three years earlier with the establishment of local authority social services departments as a focus for social work outside medical control.[2]

Whatever the logic for administering the health and personal social services as independent but internally unified services, it was in some respects contrary to that of central government policies for service development, and also to the care needs of individuals served by both professions. In both these latter respects, the case presented was for greater integration in the planning and provision of care. Yet the reorganisations arguably erected structural barriers to such integration, on top of already entrenched professional barriers. Even so, there was no lack of recognition in the official guidance to the new authorities that individual needs were not compartmentalised in ways which reflected administrative divisions.[3] In practice, many individuals have both health and social needs; the balance between them shifts over time with changes in physical and/or intellectual dependency. (The boundary between such needs is difficult to define, however, often being a construct of competing professional ideologies rather than of 'objective' assessment.) In addition, both the health and personal social services provide residential, day and domiciliary services to the same client groups, whilst other local authority, central government and non-statutory agencies also make contributions to a wider spectrum of care. Such services must be integrated at the level of individuals to ensure that they receive a mix of services appropriate to their changing needs and do not fall between the boundaries of separately administered care systems. This requirement, in turn, necessitates that planning also be coordinated so that an appropriate range and volume of services is available for the construction of individualised service packages.

Alongside the needs of individuals for comprehensive and continuous care provided across agency boundaries, are the related requirements of national policy objectives. Three are particularly relevant: the promotion of services which meet needs more appropriately than clinically unnecessary hospital stays; the development of more cost effective patterns of care, and the improvement of service standards for the long-stay client groups which have historically been neglected in resource allocation processes. Each of these objectives is closely interlinked. Taken together they effectively represent different dimensions of what has been a central policy preoccupation of successive governments: the expansion of community care. Whilst this objective has been shrouded in ambiguity[4], three aspects of it are clearly relevant to the context of this discussion. First, that it implies a shift in the balance of responsibilities and resources from the NHS to other agencies, especially social services departments; second, that the NHS is consequently dependent on the ability and willingness of such agencies to assume proportionately greater responsibilities for providing care, and, third, that service planning and delivery processes need to be more effectively integrated across agency boundaries.

Given the apparent contradiction between, on the one hand, the thrust of administrative reorganisation and, on the other, the pattern of individual needs and the demands of national policy, the immediate response of the DHSS was to emphasise the importance of health and local authorities collaborating with each other. The 1974 reorganisation aimed to facilitate this process by two means: drawing the boundaries of area health authorities to coincide with those of the local authorities responsible for personal social services ('one-to-one-coterminosity'); and placing on both sets of authority a statutory duty to collaborate through a joint consultative committee (or JCC), a body which also had a statutory basis. Although this was to be a non-executive committee, the DHSS hoped that its authority would be guaranteed by the inclusion in its membership of influential health authority members and the chairs of relevant local authority committees. Two years after reorganisation – and amid signs that the JCCs had been largely stillborn[5] – the DHSS supplemented these arrangements with the joint planning and joint finance initiatives.

Joint planning was intended to be a more specific and strategic concept than the generalised notion of collaboration which it now superseded. Accordingly, each health authority was required to establish with its matching social services authority a joint care planning team (JCPT) which would report to the JCC but be composed of officers with sufficient skills and authority to drive forward joint planning at a strategic level. The central task of the new JCPTs was defined as being 'to advise health and local authorities on the development of strategic plans and guidelines identified by the JCC as requiring a joint approach to planning'.[6] To this end, they were specifically advised not to think of joint planning 'only in terms of very short-term activities such as the preparation of budgets for one year . . . .'[7] Each JCPT could be supported by specialist sub-teams for specific client groups or issues and the whole planning machinery was exhorted to adopt a fully integrated approach. Thus DHSS guidance defined joint planning as a process in which 'each authority contributes to all stages of the other's planning, from the first step in developing common policies and strategies to the production of operational plans to carry them out'.[8] We consider below the extent to which this approach to joint planning has been successful in the ensuing decade. Before doing so, however, we discuss the second initiative undertaken by the DHSS in 1976 to provide renewed impetus for the integration of health and local authority care systems: the introduction of a financial incentive to collaborate, in the shape of the joint finance programme.

Joint finance and the 'care in the community' initiative

Joint finance is essentially an earmarked sum of money allocated annually by the DHSS to health authorities in England.[9] The programme was designed to enable short-term financial support to be provided to projects in the personal social services which are of demonstrable benefit to the health service. Since 1977, however, it has been extended to include voluntary organisations, housing, education, community health and primary health services. It appears that most of the money continues to be allocated to the personal social services, though there is evidence that at least a significant minority of health authorities is allocating substantial sums to the support of community health services.[10]

At its inception, ministers identified the primary purpose of the programme as being 'to reduce dependence on long-stay hospitals'[11] by providing the personal social services with a tangible incentive to engage with the health service in the development of community care. Its role was thus to provide both an inducement for local authorities to involve themselves in joint planning and also a budget to finance the outcome of such planning. Nonetheless, while the programme built up rapidly from £8m to £105m between 1976/7 and 1985/6, the resources available remained modest in relation to total spending on health and personal social services: in 1984/5, joint finance accounted for 0.7% and 2.8% of gross current expenditure on each service, respectively.[12] Moreover, it is equally marginal in relation to the scale of the transfer in responsibilities implied by community care policies. Consequently, there has been a succession of calls from Parliamentary and other official bodies for more substantial development funds to bridge the transition from hospital to community-based systems of care.[13] At the same time, local authorities have been faced with growing demands for care from individuals living in the community and have tended to give higher priority to such needs rather than to the discharge of patients from long-stay hospitals. The fact that the programme provided only short-term pump priming support reinforced local authority inclinations to use it for the former purpose rather than, as they saw it, to relieve health authorities from the long-term financial responsibility of maintaining the long-stay hospital system. As a result, social services rather than NHS priorities were most directly served by the programme, a conclusion reached both by the House of Commons Public Accounts Committee and also by other research.[14]

For all these reasons, therefore, joint finance has been of limited effectiveness in securing a significant shift in the balance of care and responsibilities, especially in a period of continuing economic restraint. Indeed, a further crucial limitation of the joint finance programme has been its introduction at a point when personal social services growth was being dramatically reduced: whereas their total spending increased by 63% over the five years to 1974/5, the equivalent figure was only 8% over the following five years.[15] As a result, social services departments have been reluctant to enter into the long-term revenue commitments which arise when joint finance support tapers out after the first three years. That reluctance applied generally, but was particularly strong in relation to expenditure perceived as meeting NHS or central government priorities rather than locally determined ones.

By the early 1980s central government was wishing to speed the discharge of long-stay patients to the community, and the experience of joint finance suggested that a different kind of financial mechanism would be necessary. From the local authority point of view, it would need to provide long-term financial support for patient transfers; whilst for the NHS the allocation of health service resources to local government would need to be tied to the production of services which guaranteed to relieve it of specified responsibilities. These considerations came together in the 'care in the community' initiative.

A number of options for accelerating the discharge of long-stay patients was canvassed in 1981[16] and a package of changes was announced two years later, following a prolonged period of consultation.[17] In particular, health authorities were empowered to make grants without time limit for the care of patients transferred to the community. In addition, the maximum period of 100% support for joint financed projects was extended from three to 10 years – but only for patient transfer schemes. Yet these changes were essentially of an enabling kind. Research has suggested that they were not infrequently perceived in the field as offering insufficient incentives either for local authorities to accept significantly increased numbers of discharged patients or for health authorities to transfer resources. Thus, there was a strong tendency for funds to be recycled within the health service, with the result that the scale of financial transfers has been limited. The Audit Commission has estimated that they amount to no more than £10–£20m per year.[18]

These financial changes were, however, introduced at a period of further structural upheaval within the NHS. In the first place, one-to-one coterminosity was abolished following the streamlining of NHS management arrangements in 1982, through the abolition of the area tier of administration.[19] As a result, almost half of all social services departments now relate to more than one health authority, with a fifth relating to between four and seven of them.[20] Not only were many inter-authority relationships disrupted whilst the NHS established new structures and management arrangements, but these changes also increased the administrative and time costs of collaborative planning for many local authorities. Moreover, joint planning arrangements were only just beginning to be re-established when the introduction, from 1983 onwards, of the Griffiths general management changes[21] initiated another round of administrative turbulence. In the short term, at least, these developments have hindered the growth of inter-authority relationships. As both an official working party[22] and the Audit Commission[23] have recognised, however, structural fragmentation is but one of many barriers to the provision of integrated care, and not necessarily the most substantial, as the Northern Ireland experience continues to demonstrate. Indeed, the structural unification of health and personal social services in Northern Ireland has largely been vitiated by the continuing influence of process factors, especially those born out of professional attitudes. In England, the Audit Commission has also drawn attention to the importance of process factors in promoting community care innovations whilst, at the same time, developing a powerful critique of the inconsistency in central government policies as a principal explanation for the failure to make more rapid progress towards community care goals.[25] In particular, financial policies administered by the Department of the Environment were shown to penalise local authorities which sought to expand community care provision in accordance with DHSS objectives. In addition, social security policies for which the DHSS is wholly responsible were criticised for making resources relatively freely available to fund residential care at a time when health and local authorities were being constrained from extending community services. Such structural, administrative and financial factors have been important in creating an environment which, in many respects, has been incompatible with the pursuit of integrated health and local authority planning. At the same time, however, it would be wrong either to see the record of the past decade in wholly negative terms, or to accept such factors as sufficient explanations for the difficulties which local organisations have undoubtedly faced in developing joint planning. In particular, we need to explore the kinds of processes and skills necessary for effective cross-boundary working, and question the extent to which these were recognised when the joint planning initiative was launched.

Collaborative planning: a waste of time or only a relative failure?

The accumulated evidence of research in this field suggests that collaborative planning of the kind envisaged in DHSS guidelines has not so much failed as not been attempted. In contrast to the latter's picture of health and local authorities' achieving close integration throughout all stages in the planning process[26], our own research concluded that, in general, such agencies worked separately and, at best, only in parallel with each other.[27] Other research produced similar conclusions.[28] Nonetheless, and as one of us has argued elsewhere[29], such judgements about the failure of collaborative planning are based on the circulars' view of what, in effect, would constitute absolute success in this field. Moreover, unless such assessments are also related to specified rational planning processes which most agencies only grope towards within the relative peace and security of their own boundaries.[33] Some of the difficulties and unrealities of what was expected of them can be judged from the underlying assumptions on which the rational collaborative planning model is founded. These include:

1   A systems-wide view of need and service interdependencies, rather than a perspective limited by the boundaries of a single organisation or its sub-sections.

2   A well-developed analytical capacity for identifying need, gaps in provision and alternative means of filling them.

3   A shared set of values and a broadly based consensus around ends and means, the most important element of which is a shared commitment to maximising client rather than provider benefits.

4   Sufficient goodwill, trust and altruism to allow providers to sacrifice territory, resources and service models in order to serve the higher goal of meeting service users' needs.

5   The concurrence of all these conditions at an appropriate place and time.

Merely to spell out these assumptions is to indicate what a hugely optimistic view of planning the rational model is based upon. Even if some of these preconditions can be found in isolation, the probability of finding them in combination and at an appropriate time is remote. Most fundamentally, it is a model which assumes that 'rationality is its own reward', in the sense that to be rational is to be motivated to meet user rather than organisational needs. A further weakness in this optimistic approach to planning is its over-reliance on the appropriate bureaucratic architecture, such as the coordinating committees and planning teams of the joint planning circulars, together with the authority systems of which they are a part. But planning prescriptions also need to take into account the people who inhabit such structures. Thus the most elegant structures for planning will provide only limited payoffs unless they are constructed with regard to the motivations of the people or organisations who have to operate them. The latter are generally less disinterested than the rational planning model implies – and the introduction of financial incentives like joint finance is a recognition, albeit a limited one, of that essential fact. There is a large literature showing that the formal goals of organisations are routinely displaced by those pursuing goals which are essentially concerned with the acquisition and defence of organisational resources.[34] Indeed, a much more pessimistic view of motivations and behaviour emerges from the organisation theory literature than that underpinning the optimistic prescriptions of the rational collaborative model. Drawn from power dependence and bargaining models, this pessimistic perspective particularly emphasises that:

1   Collaboration imposes costs on the organisations and individuals required to carry it out, as well as being presumed to generate benefits for individuals served by such agencies.

2   In the providers' calculus, such costs may exceed the perceived benefits of collaboration either to service users or to providers themselves.

3   People will work together when some mutual advantage is perceived.
4   Organisational life is more frequently characterised by bargaining and exchange than by rational analysis.

In other words, the pessimistic approach recognises that there is more than one rationality at work and that 'organisational rationality' – the pursuit or defence of self-interest – is just as logical as a 'user rationality' in which the maximisation of client benefits is paramount.

To recognise the power of the latter insights should not, however, be confused with advocating the abandonment of rational collaborative planning. The Joint Approach to Social Policy (JASP) research in which we were engaged[35] showed that behaviour in social service organisations is a mixture of the self-interested and the disinterested. We found that the service ethic existed as a motivating force within the health and personal social services, although it operated alongside a well-developed appreciation of what was in the best interests of providing agencies and their key personnel. Nonetheless, providing better services, no less than advancing one's own career or securing resources for one's own organisation, did prompt collaborative planning. Thus organisations did collaborate on occasions because they believed it to be in the interests of their clients rather than because some mutual advantage was to be gained from it. In addition, the architecture of the rational model provided an essential context for bargaining and exchange. Analysis and formal systems were necessary complements to wheeling and dealing. Planning machinery and coordinating arrangements proved to be a necessary (but not a sufficient) condition for collaborative planning, while a framework of shared values and objectives helped to shape, and constrain, the activities of actors jostling to secure their individual advantage or some mutual benefit.

Taken together, these findings illustrate the need to regard these optimistic and pessimistic views of planning as complementary. If it is a mistake to assume that joint planning will somehow 'happen' if only we get our structures and planning systems 'right', the rational model's emphasis on goal-setting, formal machinery, accountability and analysis provides an essential context within which more fluid, behavioural approaches can be harnessed. Positively to be encouraged, indeed, is the development of skills in identifying both tactical opportunities for exchange and the kinds of influence and motivations which shape the behaviour of key individuals in other organisations. These considerations may be brought together in suggesting that collaborative planning is more likely to be successful if elements of the two perspectives are combined.

We conclude this section, therefore, with a checklist generated by our research and which sought to treat those perspectives as complementary rather than alternative approaches to planning.[36] Our approach was to specify features of an environment for collaboration which needed to be explicitly structured whilst at the same time emphasising the kinds of tactics which also increase the likelihood of such environments producing coordinated outputs.

Strategic starting points: structuring environments for coordination

1   Establish a manageable core of formal, inter-agency machinery supported by problem-solving, time limited working groups.
2   Build senior member/chief officer participation into the formal machinery in order to: emphasise the priority of inter-agency working; give support to systems-wide thinking; underpin the moral authority of client need; ensure that joint agreements can be honoured, and structure processes of accountability so that they span agency boundaries.
3   Adopt a selective approach to the choice of issues for inter-agency planning and thus to the creation of formal working groups (ie don't bite off more than you can chew).
4   Budget for a significant, though selective, investment of staff time or external consultancy in policy analysis; budget also for adequate administrative support for formal machinery.
5   Create a 'crock of gold' – an inter-agency budget to serve as a source of incentives and as a means of tying coordination into mainstream budget allocation decisions.

Tactics for tacticians

1   Identify areas of interdependence with other agencies and hence the potential need for coordination.
2   Recognise that coordination carries costs as well as benefits and that the likelihood of interaction and its productivity will depend upon the balance of costs and benefits perceived by individuals and agencies.
3   Accept that coordination is more usually promoted by the possibility of individual/agency gain than by systems-wide/client benefit. However, system/client gain can be a powerful motive for coordination operating alongside, or even as a substitute for, individual/agency gain. Therefore, utilise the language of need and client gain wherever possible, whilst identifying any opportunity for generating more immediate gains (see below).
4   Seek to create a 'positive sum game' by identifying potential areas of gain for all participants in a given coordination arena. (NB our research suggests that a tactician may be more skilful in

identifying and anticipating the needs of other agencies than they are themselves – and may be able to convince them that they have needs of which they have not hitherto been aware.)

5 Identify ways by which such needs might be met (at the individual or agency level) and seek to create circumstances in which those individuals/agencies whose cooperation you require can secure valued benefits from interaction with you. (NB their calculation of cost and benefit may not coincide with your own: goods with a low cost to the providing agency may be perceived to be of apparently disproportionate worth by their recipients.)

6 If a positive sum game cannot be established, give up: the game's not worth the candle. Concentrate on producing single service outputs rather than joint ones and move on to potentially more productive areas for coordination.

Putting research into practice

With the completion of the research one of the authors returned to local government to resume a career in social service planning and research. Prior to the Joint Approach to Social Policy (Jasp) work this had been as a research officer within a large inner city department in the mid to late seventies. At that time collaboration had been largely a paper exercise, overly optimistic and serenely grounded in the rationality of topic papers and the production of the corporate plan.

The new post was as a manager of a staff group closely involved in planning service development, where paper plans and planning machinery were scarce but where there were real possibilities to develop schemes on the ground. Part of the attraction of the position was a lead role in formal joint planning, for which our research findings seemed at least relevant if not essential. Instead of being on the outside and hypothesising and then concluding from observation, inference and interview, it was now to be as an insider. This would still mean hypothesising but as a participant, having to live with the results.

Whilst not always explicitly testing the prescriptions out they did provide a basis for some early thinking about the collaborative scene and what might be a fruitful direction and what should be avoided. This is what is explored in the remainder of the chapter, where we begin by looking at the background to collaboration in the new authority, followed by some consideration of what seemed to be barriers to interaction and where significant opportunities rested. We then move to ways of putting collaboration into practice by structuring the environment and being prepared to act tactically.

Collaboration in context

The setting was an outer London borough, where housing, education, social services and physical planning were subject to one corporate authority. In this instance it was a Conservative administration, with a recent history of pursuing rate restraint as a positive policy, before the imposition of central controls and penalties. However, a corollary was that avenues were sought to diversity expenditure on to others' accounts: Urban Programme, Section 11 Grant, DHSS Welfare Benefits and, of course, Joint Finance. In that sense the local authority were outward looking and amenable to further diversification and local sharing. Additionally there were highly skilled and confident politicians, an important feature when discussing collaboration in this context.

The District Health Authority (DHA) was coterminous with borough boundaries with poor physical and outmoded acute hospital stock and in the very difficult position of being a potential gainer within a RAWP losing region. Both the health and local authorities started from a relatively low resource and service base, with a lot to fear from interaction that might inflict resource reduction yet able to see the potential benefits for collaboration.

By contrast and almost by compensation, the local voluntary and private sectors were burgeoning, the latter in residential and private sector sheltered accommodation, with residential and nursing homes benefiting from formerly highly local DHSS limits – the local authority had lobbied for these to seek high quality care. The voluntary service sector was largely developed from the organisational bases of church and religious groups with funding secured from the Greater London Council and the Manpower Services Commission, to the extent that the combined budgets were almost the same as that of the formal social services. Several groups had national reputations and others with aspirations stretching beyond the borough. Hence, the private and voluntary sector were a force to be reckoned with. Yet they were at that time only very tenuously linked into local service planning and certainly distant from formal collaborative planning.

Not that this was in any vibrant form, for in late 1983 joint planning had not yet recovered from NHS re-organisation, only the Joint Consultative Committee (JCC) and Joint Care Planning Team (JCPT) were functioning. Partly this resulted from administrative inertia, but also from a lack of credibility in joint exercises stemming from the key experience under the Area Health Authority. Then a massive care planning exercise, with large groups meeting over three years, had produced a variety of aspirational plans in time for the demise of the Authority. There were, however, other reasons why inter-authority relations were at a low ebb.

Barriers and opportunities

From an optimistic perspective it would be enough to know that some machinery was in place to begin to move toward producing integrated plans and policies. However, from the Jasp research we knew how important it was in assessing collaborative potential to first identify what seemed to be hindering or obstructing collaboration, what were the barriers. Knowing these helped to make sense of the costs and benefits that operating the machinery might produce or indeed the currency of equivalence that might aid exchange or draw up the lines for conflict.

Similarly we needed to identify what was likely to promote collaboration, what were partners valuing from contacts, where were the openings that could at least lead to a start in joint planning. It was also appreciated that working around barriers, if successful, opened up opportunities. This was certainly true in this instance of the main barrier to effective collaboration: political factors.

These political considerations developed from the administrative complexity of the locality, for despite nominal coterminosity the 1982 re-organisation had, through extra-territorial management, left one third of the borough population receiving local acute services from a neighbouring DHA. There was, therefore, a clear logistical barrier, especially in service planning for elderly people, in drawing together effective groups spanning hospital and community services from two DHA's and two sets of consultants with different ideologies of care. In the event even that was manageable, if not very productive. The greatest single barrier arose from the fact that the majority political group had its heartland in that one third of the borough, with large numbers of elderly people and with some important elderly members or members with relatives in the area. Hence, there was direct experience of the neighbouring DHA's 'rationalisation' of the acute sector. This meant in practice the closure of local, small units, some with GP beds, that primarily met the needs of an older generation. Add to this increased pressure on the borough's services and the result was conflict.

Across the remainder of the borough and the main collaborative forums, there was as a result a guardedness and an uncertainty if not a basic lack of trust. The borough placed enough significance in health service matters to establish their own Health Service Liaison Committee to monitor and relate pro-actively to the NHS. Overall collaboration and joint planning became highly politicised. In terms of barriers and opportunities this worked both ways; it hindered interaction but at the same time gaining senior member attention was not difficult and if deals could be negotiated they could quickly be ratified.

Having highlighted one of the barriers it is worth mentioning a number of opportunities, at a resource and officer level, which combined to suggest that selective joint planning might be worthwhile. Firstly the resource position.

Whilst low resource bases were mirrored in low service stocks, opportunities for collaboration were created by asymmetries in these between agencies. For example, the borough contained a large psychiatric hospital scheduled for retrenchment. The local authority, in common with others, had very limited mental health services; the DHA wished to release the resources tied up in buildings, the borough to develop a nucleus of community based care.

In a reversal of that pattern, the DHA had very little investment in services for people with a mental handicap, yet financial responsibility for people in out-borough hospitals. The borough had some range and depth to their services but needed to expand to support better quality services and to better meet the needs of carers. Such were the potential grounds for exchange – or conflict.

In terms of personnel, low resources meant small bureaucracies, with flat hierarchies. In some instances this meant actors had little time for extra-agency activities, it very much depended upon how they weighed up the likely benefits for their service systems from participation, as to whether it was worthwhile. For those who did, primarily in mental health and services for people with a mental handicap, it meant that those involved were central to the management of their own organisations, there being no resources for peripheral liaison roles. Also, participants often combined developmental with operational responsibilities, and so planning reflected future thinking together with current frontline experience. Moreover in a small locality there were plenty of occasions for informal contact – or they were not too difficult to arrange – and together with the small number of clearances needed for action through compact agencies, meant that ideas could be fed rapidly into formal arenas and decisions made quickly.

Developing local joint planning: structuring environments

With these barriers and potential opportunities in mind we now review these aspects of the prescriptive framework (listed on page 21–22) that were applied directly or indirectly within the locality. It should be stressed at this point that this was a joint exercise involving, through discussion and debate, a number of local planners and voluntary sector activists about how, where and whether to progress joint matters. Also, at later points others were involved in the sense of taking part in the operation of the machinery and also, by decision, overriding others' agreements or arrangements.

Formal core of inter-agency machinery

The JCC and JCPT were in position and managing the joint finance (JF) budget. When the distribution of this became problematic and there looked to be difficulties for the chairman of the DHA, a leading councillor within the majority group, a move to establish care planning teams was made. For the borough, involved in a major dispute with the DHA next door over hospital closures, some area of relative policy calm was important. Two problem solving time limited teams were established. These used a variation of the Delphi technique to open up problem areas and then concentrated on those which could only be resolved by more than one agency working together – a means of highlighting inter-dependencies. Single service solutions were to be implemented through the relevant agencies. Teams met for three months and implementation progress assessed after one year.

Senior member/chief officer participation

To an extent this had been built in the previous Area Health Authority (AHA) days but it was built upon as a result of the political importance of collaboration. The JCPT was high powered on both sides with the borough team led by the chief executive with the directors of finance, education, social services and housing. This induced the DHA to field the majority of their Management Board. Planners attended in a support role. The JCC matched this with the respective service chairmen from the borough and the chairman and vice chairman of the DHA. More recently the voluntary sector representatives, some active in the care planning teams as well, have joined the JCC, with one impact being the claim for a voluntary seat on the JCPT. This was accepted and raised voluntary sector membership of the JCPT to two as one person already chaired a planning team on mental health matters.

One of the merits of a strong political lead in collaboration was the space it created for middle and more junior staff to get on and do the more detailed joint planning and the negotiations needed to produce results: any untoward developments could always be unscrambled in the JCPT or failing that, between chairmen of the DHA and the Health Liaison Committee before JCC.

Selectivity and budgeting for policy and administrative time

In getting joint planning going and more importantly keeping it going, these issues were crucial. From a bottom up perspective there was pressure to set up teams across the board: those working together wanted to plan projects and get access to resources. The planners, however, calculated that only two teams at any one time could be meeting, for very practical reasons. Firstly, many of the key personnel (such as medical and nursing staff, housing and social services managers) would need to be present in both teams and possibly all of them. Progress could not be made without them and neither could their time and commitment be abused at the expense of other duties. Selectivity was a crucial selling point for some other participants particularly education with memories and experience of the previous exercise.

Secondly, two teams were the maximum which could be supported within the planning and administrative resources available. In this there was an acknowledged exchange; the borough supplying planners, the DHA with fewer of these but relatively more administrative and secretarial staff. The latter minuted and managed the arrangement of meetings (the most time consuming and thankless of tasks but absolutely critical to sustaining commitment and continuity), the borough staff working on papers and supplying and seeking joint information in between meetings. More recently, with more work going through the core machinery, a jointly financed joint planning officer has been employed, with a servicing and progress chasing role.

Resource incentives

The joint planning structure was tied into the joint finance timetable and main programme resource schedules. Projects had to either have been considered by the team or relate clearly to both the philosophy of service development and the identified priorities. This provided a clear incentive for participation and even now that the joint finance programme is relatively silted up, the ability to pre-bid remains important. It is important for that programme and to signal to the parent agency or committee that a joint need has been established which helps in substantiating claims for main programme resources.

To date there have been no inter-agency budgets identified to act as crocks of gold, which is perhaps a measure of the state of collaborative play: resources come from one agency or on a one-off basis from both, matters are not sufficiently integrated to sustain long term, long standing, independent budgets. However, progress was being made in what might be seen as a halfway measure, the negotiation of a resource transfer package between the authorities. The whole discussion about resource and patient transfers had begun to transform joint planning, moving it beyond general statements of policy intent to reviewing the needs of identified and named individuals and how those needs were to be met. This applied for people in hospital and for those in the community who might qualify to fill a vacant place in a transfer scheme.

Acting tactically

Working out and working within a structure designed to enable collaboration was a first step. In the event this was not too difficult to achieve and having established a pattern, not too difficult to sustain. If nothing else the slow process of mutual learning about operational styles, values and professional differences had been embarked upon.

However, to realise integrated policies or practices required attention to those aspects of interaction that we have termed tactics. Basically, these consist of actors to collaboration or coordination thinking through and thinking around the costs and benefits of interaction. Tactics require actors to be self conscious in their behaviour and at the least to be able to take the role of the other, to see the world from another's perspective. Without this ability it is all too easy to create barriers and blockages to integration needlessly and be left defending a professional or partisan domain for its own sake. Seeing the world from the other side allows the participant to identify other's costs and more importantly, what benefits might be valued and sought which would allow a concerted effort at integration to go ahead. Or it may identify where events are likely to be so prohibitively costly that it would be advisable to seek developments in another policy field or with other agencies.

Identifying interdependence

Identifying interdependence is a necessary first step both because it highlights where agencies may seek services from each other or because it shows there is no interdependence and agencies can go it alone. Within the borough the importance of joint assessment for elderly people between health, housing and social services for their respective bed and accommodation spaces was a clear area of overlap. Also for the different services for elderly mentally ill (EMI) people in a variety of settings. It is important to draw out the links between services because they are often not clearly appreciated. Identification also allows the publication and proclamation of them and some of the potential costs of going it alone, ie: poor assessment, misplacements or poor quality care. One technique that proved useful, which starts from individuals' needs, was the drawing up of a balanced service system, based on the work of John O'Brien.[37] Using this within the borough it was possible to clearly identify for

EMI services where health and social services needed to work together but the attempt to provide joint centres or shared day places foundered. Instead it was agreed to develop a joint policy to be implemented from geographically separate centres with different catchment areas: with little existing service provision there were more than enough clients for each centre.

Costs and benefits of coordination

In the above example whilst all the participants to the planning of day services to elderly mentally ill people saw the logic of integrated provision the costs in terms of slippage on separate capital programmes and the power of a newly appointed consultant to defend separation of medical and social functions meant that a different service resulted. For the consultant mixing functions muddled boundaries and introduced vagaries into practice. It also opened up the issue of who would run such integrated facilities. For the borough the benefits would have been in on site medical assessment, better care and a more effective use of capital resources. However, given the overall level of need the outcome was acceptable and showed that in this instance it was better to produce single service outputs rather than engage in protracted conflict. Besides the consultant was a community services ally and there was little point in sacrificing future cooperation on what was fast becoming a zero-sum equation.

The example also shows some of the more general features of coordination that apply in other settings and for policy as well as project development: the costs of sharing control, of compromise, of disturbance and to notions of tidiness. At an individual level these can affect career or even a person's ego to the extent that some actors feel personally at risk or threatened by plans for coordination or integration. It is not the case that these are always present but it is worth remembering when what appear to be irrational blockages are encountered in joint planning, for example, never receiving a superior's clearance from a subordinate representative or un-explained absences from meetings.

Valued benefits

If some of the personal costs were on the down side within the borough there were more positive aspects concerning valued benefits. Housing, for example, firmed up their caring role through continued involvement in special needs housing at a time of decline in general needs. More positively the Housing Improvement Programme (HIPS) bid was levered up, which even if the allocation did not always allow for special needs on the necessary scale, did protect other aspects of the housing and improvement programme from the depredations of central government. Housing were also able to monitor who else might be moving into the housing field – group homes and shared dwellings, where they might more reasonably in normalisation terms be landlords than say, social services. For the latter maintenance and repairs were then shifted to the housing revenue account.

For the NHS the value of joint planning and development was high. Firstly, there was the promise of potential resource gains through the joint finance programme which had previously been dominated by the borough. Secondly, the attraction lay in drawing in the borough to discussions on care planning for priority groups. This was important because plans for a new DGH looked likely to absorb most, if not all, of their development allocation. At the outset, service planning for mental health and for people with a mental handicap definitely improved with the openness of the DHA in relations with the borough and voluntary sector: a share in existing and future resources was offered, as was a share in the ownership of the policy areas and the future shape of services. Reinforcing these moves were two other factors which altered the pre-1983 cost benefit equation: general management and the regional review process. Collaboration with local authorities and the voluntary sector were stressed in the latter and used by the former to secure review goals. To do this managers needed to begin to shift the focus of action away from institutional care and from existing power and professional bases to community organisations and emergent groups, such as CPN's.

Voluntary agencies also perceived the value of participating in joint planning and collaborative ventures. Their profile was upped to the extent of their real contribution to community based care: they were major service providers and were now seen to be and treated as partners. Having gained that recognition they now had access to the formal and informal decision making forums of both statutory agencies and the opportunity to redirect policies and resources. Of particular interest were joint finance and the main programme monies of the DHA. For both the health and local authority the voluntary sector represented a third force that it was better to have on the inside. They could be aligned with if need be to pressurise the other authority and they were an alternative to either self development, where this was difficult, or to test out innovative services, for example, care attendants or the running of a management committee by users of a day facility for disabled people.

Positive sum games

Over time, and part of the ability to act tactically may comprise waiting and deferring benefits, valued aspects of interaction in different policy areas came into line: there was something for most if not all. Contrarily where it was perceived that the benefit was one sided or such that only by one partner accepting costs could others accrue benefits, interaction was diminished or indeed ceased altogether. A local example concerned services for elderly people where the DHA had a normative shortage of long stay beds. Proclamations (by the DHA) of a joint issue and the importance of community care were perceived as load-shedding by the borough, to the extent that a zero-sum game opened up, and there were no mutual advantages for the borough, either in service terms or crucially in political terms. The DHA perceived the unwieldy and cumbersome nature of the planning machinery to be at fault, and proposed an alternative analytical device involving a service coordinator who would develop a joint strategy and push its implementation when agreed. For this to happen the borough will need to be moved from their view that it is a single service problem for the DHA; the DHA will need to rethink the cost-benefit equation and attempt to create a positive sum environment for residential services for elderly people.

Lessons learned

Whilst some aspects of service development for elderly people have been blocked, policy statements for disabled people, people with a mental handicap or mental health problems have been published and more positive developments have been derived through local collaborative mechanisms. For example, specialist housing with extra care facilities for disabled people, extra care sheltered housing, a joint information system for mentally handicapped people, clear direction and housing projects for mentally ill people through a standing mental health planning team.

It may be now though that the days of formalised joint planning in terms of planning teams sitting down and solving problems and broadly conforming to the rational model in outline but using the processes derived from the more pessimistic model, of exchange and bargaining, are numbered. Such a process for making progress in inter-agency planning seemed appropriate for the late 1970s and early 1980s. It provided a mechanism for tackling broad policy issues and for overcoming the difficulties of having little or no conventions for planning between agencies. Now seems the time for change and experimentation with different models. In some respects the overall costs of integration are proving to be too high and single service responsibility models, such as the local authority control of services for people with a mental handicap, mental health services for the health authority, may be the way forward. This does not mean the failure of joint planning per se but its location in a particular time and space. The Jasp model made more of a reality of idealised processes and emphasised the importance of tying joint development into service management and political processes. The single service model will certainly rely, during handover on negotiating skills, and for impact on management and political factors. Whilst the means must remain relative the outcomes of better quality care should stay positively universal.

Acknowledgement

The chapter is in part based upon SSRC funded research which the authors conducted with colleagues at the University of Bath, Loughborough University of Technology and the Royal Institute of Public Administration.

References

1 DHSS (1970), *National Health Service: The Future Structure of the National Health Service*, London, HMSO.
2 Social Services Departments were established in 1971 following the recommendations of the (Seebohm 1968) *Report of the Committee on Local Authority and Allied Personal Social Services*, cmnd, 3703, London, HMSO.
3 DHSS (1972), *Management Arrangements for the Reorganised NHS*, para 3.25, London, HMSO.
4 See DHSS (1981), *Report of a Study on Community Care*, London, Department of Health and Social Security; and Walker, A (1982), 'The Meaning and Social Division of Community Care' in Walker, A (ed), *Community Care*, Basil Blackwell and Martin Robertson.
5 DHSS (1976), *Joint Consultative Committee Review: 31 March 1976*, rp 2, London, Department of Health and Social Services.
6 DHSS (1977), *Joint Care Planning: Health and Local Authorities*, circular HC(77) 17/LAC(77)10, para 4, London, Department of Health and Social Security.
7 *Ibid.*
8 *Ibid.*, para 1.
9 Somewhat different arrangements exist in Scotland and Wales: see Hunter, D and Wistow, G (1987), *Community Care in Britain: Variations on a Theme*, London, King's Fund.

10   See National Audit Office (1987), *Community Care Developments*, Report by the Comptroller and Auditor General, HC 108, London, HMSO; and Wistow, G, Hardy, B and Turrell, A (1988), *Collaboration Under Financial Constraint*, Gower.

11   Castle, B (1975) *Speech to National Association of Health Authorities*, 11 July.

12   House of Commons Social Services Committee (1985–87), *Public Expenditure on the Social Services*, HC 387, vol II, p 27, London, HMSO.

13   See House of Commons Social Services Committee (1985), *Community Care*, Second Report, 1984–5, HC13, London, HMSO; Working Group on Joint Planning (1985), *Progress in Partnership*, London, DHSS; Audit Commission (1986), *Making a Reality of Community Care*, London, HMSO; and National Audit Office (1987), *op cit.*

14   House of Commons Committee of Public Accounts (1983), *Department of Health and Social Security: The Joint Financing of Care by the National Health Service and Local Government*, Eighth Report, 1982–3, HC160, London, HMSO; and Wistow, G (1987), 'Joint Finance: Promoting a New Balance of Care and Responsibilities in England?', in *International Journal of Social Psychiatry*, vol 33, no 2, 1987, pp 83–91.

15   Webb, A and Wistow, G (1981), 'The Personal Social Services: Incrementalism, Expediency or Systematic Social Planning?' in Walker, A (ed), *Public Expenditure and Social Policy*, p 145, London, Heinemann.

16   DHSS (1981), *Care in the Community: A Consultative Document on Transferring Resources for Care in England*, London, Department of Health and Social Security.

17   DHSS (1981b), *Health Service Development: Care in the Community and Joint Finance*, circular HC(83)6/LAC(83)5, London, Department of Health and Social Security.

18   Audit Commission (1986), *op cit*, para 70.

19   DHSS and Welsh Office (1979), *Patients First: Consultative Paper on the Structure and Management of the NHS in England and Wales*, London, HMSO.

20   Wistow, G and Fuller, S (1986), *Collaboration Since Restructuring: the 1984 Survey of Joint Planning and Joint Finance*, Loughborough, Centre for Research in Social Policy and National Association of Health Authorities, p 56.

21   Griffiths, R (1983), *NHS Management Inquiry: Report*, London, Department of Health and Social Security.

22   Working Group on Joint Planning (1985), *op cit.*

23   Audit Commission (1986), *op cit.*

24   Connolly, M (1985), 'Has Integration Worked? The Health and Personal Social Services in Northern Ireland' in Harrison, A and Gretton, J (eds), *Health Care UK 1985*, London, Policy Journals.

25   Audit Commission (1986), *op cit*, paras 61–5.

26   DHSS (1977), *op cit*, para 4.

27   Jasp Team (1984), *Joint Approach to Social Policy: Report of Research Funded by SSRC*, Bath, University of Bath, University of Loughborough and Royal Institute of Public Administration, mimeo, p 322. A revised

version of this report is published as Challis, L; Fuller, S; Henwood, M; Klein, R; Plowden, W; Webb, A; Whittingham, P; and Wistow, G (1988), *Joint Approaches to Social Policy*, Cambridge, Cambridge University Press.

28 See, for example, Norton, A and Rogers, S (1981), 'The Health Service and Local Government Service', in McLachlan, G (ed), *Matters of Moment*, Oxford, Oxford University Press; Booth, T (1981), 'Collaboration between the Health Service and Social Services', in *Policy and Politics*, 9(1)1981, pp 23–9 and 9(2)1981, pp 205–26; Glennerster, H with Korman, N and Marslen-Wilson, F (1983), *Planning for Priority Groups*, Oxford, Martin Robertson; Wright, J and Sheldon, F (1985), 'Health and Social Services Planning', *Social Policy and Administration*, 19(3) 1985, pp 258–72.

29 Wistow, G (1988), 'Health and Local Authority Collaboration: Lessons and Prospects' in Wistow, G and Brooks, T (eds) (1988), *Joint Planning and Joint Management,* London, Royal Institute of Public Administration.

30 *Ibid.*

31 Jasp Team (1984), *op cit.*

32 Wistow (1988), *op cit.*

33 On the difficulty of introducing rational planning systems into the National Health Service, see for example, Haywood, S and Alaszewski, A (1980), 'Crisis in the Health Service', London, Croom Helm; and Lee, K and Mills, A (1982), *Policy-Making and Planning in the Health Sector*, London, Croom Helm.

34 See, for example, Benson, J K (1975), 'The Interorganisational Network as a Political Economy', in *Administrative Science Quarterly*, 20,1975, pp 229–48.

35 Jasp Team (1984), *op cit.*

36 *Ibid.*

37 Dorgan, R E and O'Brien, J (1979) *Introduction to the Balanced Service System*, Clinton, Oklahoma, Responsive Systems Associates Inc.

2 The informal care network

Nick Miller

Since the mid-1970s there has been growing interest among organisations providing health and personal social services in the relationship between their services and informal care. Increasing numbers of more dependent adults are now living outside a residential care or hospital setting. For statutory services this has required a shift of focus to collaboration with existing support networks, and provision of 'packages of care' from a variety of different sources, especially involving unpaid and largely untrained carers.

Health and social care assessments and interventions vary considerably in the sharpness of their focus on the networks of care and support surrounding the individual client/patient. Positive collaborative working with informal carers requires special techniques and skills. Benefits derived from services by clients' carers have tended to be seen as incidental and carers' views of the appropriateness of these services are rarely heard.

This chapter examines the progress in integrating formal and informal care and some of the problems this integration presents.

Definitions

There are several comprehensive reviews of informal care now available.[1] It is not the purpose of this chapter to reiterate their findings. Nevertheless some degree of definition is necessary at the outset to clarify what is meant by 'informal care'.

Abrams has defined informal care as encompassing 'the provision of help, support and protection to others by lay members of society acting in everyday domestic and occupational settings' (Abrams 1978).[2] 'Help and support' covers a range of tasks including personal care, domestic care and occasional help with transport, gardening, etc. It also encompasses 'surveillance' and a broad range of 'social support', including 'being a good neighbour' and generally 'keeping in touch'. Informal care may be sustained over a lengthy period of time or may only involve an occasional more or less one-off task.

Abrams' definition of informal carers as 'lay members of society' includes members of a family caring for one another as well as care from neighbours and friends. It may also 'shade' into individuals whose contact with the person being cared for derives from some degree of organisation (volunteers from a church or other organisation, 'good neighbours', etc). It can also include self-help groups, either of carers, eg families with mentally or physically handicapped children, or of sufferers from a specific disease or condition.

Informal care can also include 'lay' people acting in a paid capacity. Statutory services are increasingly setting up 'substitute informal care' arrangements where some payment is made and which 'imitate' informal care arrangements. Examples include sheltered housing wardens, street wardens, foster parents, paid helpers in the Kent Community Care Project model[3], adult home sharers, etc. Some landladies providing board and lodgings or supervising group homes and some owners of residential hotels fulfil a 'quasi-informal care' role for mentally ill and mentally handicapped adults being discharged from long-stay hospitals. There certainly is evidence that many individuals acting in a paid capacity (such as home helps) provide considerably more care on an 'informal' basis than is formally expected of them.

Key findings of published research

Studies focused specifically on informal care arrangements have been rare until very recently. For the most part the knowledge we have of informal care derives from studies of a given population group (such as clients of a social services office) or of service recipients (such as people entering residential care) where informal support has been but one focus of wider research. The following list provides some of the key studies where there is evidence of the relationship between self-care, informal care and formal care[4]:

1 *Social Services Clientele Studies*
   Black et al, Hadley and McGrath, Bayley et al.
2 *Patient/Client Group Studies*
   Elderly people living at home: Hunt, Tinker, Wenger, Sinclair, Levin.
   People with mental handicaps living at home: Bayley.
   Physically handicapped children and their families: Glendinning, Hatch.

People with mental illnesses: Vaughn and Leff, Grad and Sainsbury.
3   *Studies of Types of Intervention*
Short-term relief care: Allen.
Day care: Carter.
Family-based respite care for children with disabilities: Robinson, Stalker.
Kent Community Care Project model: Davies & Challis.
Adult home-sharing: Thornton and Moore.
Volunteers: Abrams.
Support at home: Bristow, Maitland and Tutt.
Self-help groups: Hatch, Vincent.

Any attempt to select common themes from this varied literature risks over-simplification. Nevertheless, some key findings seem to recur and, as we shall see, have a significant bearing on how far formal and informal care can be related.

1   Most care in the community is carried out by informal carers and is largely 'invisible' to formal caring agencies. Most informal carers appear to care without any regular 'formal' care input from formal agencies. Much formal care is focused on those who cannot count on informal support.
2   Most informal care is carried out by close relatives and the majority is provided by relatives living in the same house as the person cared for. Where care does come from outside the household, if it is needed on a regular and frequent basis, not surprisingly it will be provided by people living near at hand. Support (by occasional contact on the telephone and infrequent visits) may well be provided by those further afield.
3   A significant proportion of relatives are caring alone and experience substantial strain, eg in disturbed nights, physical tasks, emotional strains, etc.
4   Most principal carers are women: men may care for a disabled or infirm spouse or child but are unlikely to do so for other relatives. Some handicapped parents are primarily cared for by their children of school age.
5   Neighbours tend to be most frequently involved in 'surveillance' and 'auxiliary care' rather than personal care and regular domestic tasks.
6   Where there are formal care inputs which assist informal carers, often these inputs are of short duration and are limited in their scope and focus, providing only a partial response to the needs of the carers or of those cared for.
7   Formal care involvement often appears to occur on an arbitrary basis: more individuals with greater degrees of incapacity are not

receiving help than are doing so, even allowing for differences in informal support.

8 When needs for physical care and domestic support are similar, those living alone with no relatives nearby will tend to receive formal care assistance more frequently than those living with relatives or with relatives close at hand.

9 When carers are resident there is some evidence of greater formal help being provided where the tasks are heaviest on the carer, but often service allocators view the needs of those living alone as the priority for service inputs.

10 Most studies suggest that the scope for introducing informal carers to reduce the tasks of formal care is limited, though fears that informal carers pull out of caring if formal care is provided seem largely ungrounded. This may reflect the distinct roles of formal care inputs.

11 Demographic change and the increase in women working tend to suggest that there will be a decline in the amount of informal care from family members for the increasing numbers of the very elderly. Many of the carers for the very elderly are elderly themselves. How far this decline may be offset by other forms of informal care is difficult to judge, though it is unlikely that the substitution will cover the same range of 'heavy' input, particularly for the very frail and the mentally infirm.

Problems of integrating formal and informal care

The research findings summarised above highlight both the vital contribution of informal carers and the difficulties of ensuring that they receive appropriate and timely support from formal care services. Criticisms which recur in discussions with carers about services[5] are that:

1 The contribution of informal carers is often ignored by professionals.

2 Assessment criteria are too rigid and often exclude cases of real need.

3 The times at which services are available, and the tasks which can be undertaken, severely limit the relevance of formal care inputs to many informal carers.

4 Change to service allocations so as to meet changing needs is difficult to negotiate, often involving distant decision-makers, a lack of appreciation of the changing circumstances, and time delays.

The research tends to suggest that the more dependent the

person being cared for by informal carers, the more these shortcomings of existing services are apparent. Consequently, the real and felt burden on the carer may often not be lessened by formal care inputs.

How are these failures of formal care agencies being addressed? Three trends are discernible:

Political changes

There is increased pressure in the political arena to ensure that carers are adequately supported in their task. Examples of developments include proposals for a Carers Charter from both the Alliance and Labour parties, the recognition of rights of informal carers under the 1983 Mental Health Act, the widening of invalid care allowance to include married women, following prolonged litigation, and the passage of the Disabled Persons (Services, Consultation and Representation) Act 1986.

Voluntary and self-help initiatives

Self-help groups for people with particular handicaps and their carers are growing in numbers and effectiveness both at a national level and locally. For example, the development over 10 years of Crossroads Care Attendant Schemes (now operating in over 100 areas with a further 40 groups planned) has provided significant support to carers[6].

Changes in statutory services

There have been pronounced shifts in the ways that established services are provided by formal care agencies. In social services departments, for example, development of the traditional home help service into much more of a domiciliary care service in many areas has widened the range of tasks and responsiveness of this key service for more dependent clients and their carers. 'Intensive home care' specialist services are now found in most local authorities. The development of short-term relief care for mentally and physically handicapped children and elderly people away from their homes, so as in part to relieve carers, is also widespread.

Day care services provide a variety of support services which can assist carers. They have seen considerable growth, often involving partnership between statutory and voluntary bodies, with an increasing emphasis on the provision of ancillary services to meet the needs of the most dependent. A wide range of family centres and mental health resource centres have been opened in an attempt to provide a more flexible and open access service, often with support groups for carers.

A recent extension of traditional social services department support to elderly clients is the Kent Community Care Scheme. This was established to provide alternative care in the community for elderly people considered to need residential care. Social workers are provided with a limited budget for each client, which they can use as they consider appropriate to purchase a variety of forms of community care to support the elderly person at home alongside informal care support, if any. Responsibility, authority and account-ability for managing the elements of care are given to the relevant social worker, who in effect becomes the case manager. Although the report of the first evaluation of such a scheme from Kent indicates that only a relatively few clients were supported by informal carers to any extent, replications of the model elsewhere in the country suggest that support to such carers from this sort of scheme is both effective and well received.

In the health arena, some hospital beds for geriatric and elderly mentally ill patients may be committed on a rota basis to relieve carers for a short period (as well as providing rehabilitation and observation). In some instances day hospital places may be used to the same ends. Commitment to support of relatives is also evident in the growth of the hospice movement. Health care professionals have pioneered support groups for relatives of those suffering from specific conditions, (eg stroke patients, the elderly, mentally ill, etc).

There is considerable variation between localities (even within the same local or health authority) in how far such developments have occurred in the statutory or voluntary sectors. Initiatives are often 'experimental' and find demand outstripping available resources.

Addressing the problems of integration

From our accumulated knowledge of informal care, what issues seem to most need attention within formal care agencies if informal carers are to be provided with more appropriate and effective support?

Changing attitudes

Professionals in formal care agencies at all levels need to review regularly the extent to which their services relate to 'consumer' and 'carer' needs. Positive training and continuing reinforcement is needed as regards the collaborative role of services with carers, rather than focusing on the service offered to client or patient in isolation. This may well involve coping with criticism and challenges from carers. Policy and practice guidance may be needed to strike the appropriate balance between exploitation of carers and providing support equitably between those in need of it. The exercising of choice by clients/patients as to where care might come from should also be seen as a norm.

Developing assessment skills

Making formal care services more responsive to the specific needs of informal carers presupposes a clear assessment of the situation of each case. Although there is considerable literature in the field of social work theory about comprehensive assessment, evidence from research studies tends to suggest that social workers are often not particularly effective in identifying the members of their clients' social network and in assessing their respective contributions to the support of their client. The same shortcomings are probably found in much of the health service. Evidence suggests that very often assessments are carried out with one particular service in mind, eg occupational therapy, or home help, or nursing support, and informal carers find that their particular needs and circumstances do not feature significantly in the assessment or in the suggested response.

Information and training

Carers frequently complain that finding out about available support services requires perseverance, rather than being readily volunteered by professionals. Often information is passed on by other carers, as is practical advice on the caring task and its implications. Practical training in daily tasks (like lifting and management of incontinence) as well as an explanation of handicaps and their implications are still the exception rather than the rule.

Contract negotiation and teamwork

The role of organising and managing one or more of the formal support services which are designed to mesh with informal care inputs involves the important task of 'contract negotiation'[7]. Where services are provided on a 'take it or leave it' basis, clearly this sort of skill is not particularly needed; where, however, a more complex set of arrangements is required, dependent on a variety of inputs from different people at different times with different skills, then far more attention to this particular issue is required. Drawing on a clear and detailed assessment, the workers need to be able to guarantee an appropriate set of formal care inputs and to relate to the contribution of informal carers. Inevitably, the changing circumstances of the person being cared for, and of the informal carers, may require regular reviews with participation from all parties and an ability to vary the 'contract' to take account of changing circumstances. In drawing up the contract, it is critical that the professionals do not undermine informal carers and provide an effective 'enabling' supportive input.

Accessible services

If informal carers are to be adequately supported, and formal services are to be flexible and responsive to change in the 'package' of support being provided to the individual, there is a strong argument that management of care in normal circumstances needs to be as local as possible. Studies of patch-based services in the social services have argued that effectiveness depends to a large extent on the local office's being allowed autonomy and flexibility in service provision.[8] Increased awareness of available services (both among the community at large and among key professionals such as GPs) and an ability to integrate with local care networks should result.

But the case has yet to be made conclusively. Beresford and Croft have undertaken one study of social services in a patch-based authority which has seriously questioned the impact of this model of organisation on the wide range of groups providing care.[9] Others have questioned whether the patch-based approach leads to a loss of specialist skill (among social workers in particular). Such a model of working is particularly vulnerable to staff turnover. For elderly people living at home, Sinclair and others have argued that it might be more appropriate to provide a patch-based home help service, with social workers (being fewer in number) continuing to work from the traditional area office.[10]

The primary healthcare team plays a key role in the care of many dependent individuals in the community and its members have natural links with informal carers. Thus the strengthening of the group practice or health centre as a base for service delivery may prove an effective way of strengthening support to informal care. Devolution of a variety of responsibilities to GPs and the allocation of other health service staff, including paramedical staff, covering populations of some 25,000–30,000 is being experimented with in many district health authorities.[11] The creation of Cumberlege neighbourhood nursing teams and the decentralisation of other professionals working in community units are moves in the same direction.

Flexible and appropriate services

As carers cope at home with dependent children and adults who might in earlier times have been provided with 24-hour, multifaceted hospital or residential care, so support to them will need to run parallel with such care. Hence, for example, the advent of 'getting up' and 'tucking up' services for elderly and disabled people at home, together with nightsitting and night care (as opposed to day care). The positive aspects of informal care (such as its flexibility, speedy response and one-to-one nature) are what is looked for, rather than an institutional model involving rigid routines and a 'production line' approach.

The problems of effectively integrating a set of services, each provided on a large scale with competing responsibilities to other clients/patients, are enormous.[12] The more extensive and intensive the needs for external support, the stronger the case for simplifying the management of the variety of inputs.

Managing integration in the statutory agencies: better practice

Increasingly, statutory services managers are having to confront a number of key issues in relation to the integration of their services with informal care.

Information for service planning and review

The emergence latterly of particular pressure groups which highlight the problems of informal carers has exposed the difficulties that statutory service planners and providers have in gathering information about the real, but often 'invisible', needs of clients and their carers.

Although large numbers of clients and patients are dealt with by services at any point in time where carers are also providing a significant input, conveying the views of these carers to decision-makers is problematic. Carers may lack the knowledge of where and when to express their needs, and may consequently express them inappropriately or to professionals whose primary concern with the client/patient may 'block out' the carer's viewpoint. In some instances, of course, carers themselves may not be able to express their needs through fear of seeming uncaring or inadequate. In other cases, carers may fulfil their own needs through the dependency of the person being cared for.

Whilst small scale surveys of informal carers can provide some indication of the need for additional or altered services, it is much more difficult in planning to take into account the contribution of informal care at the level of a community. The availability of relatives nearby and a high level of population stability in a given community may well mean that support networks will lessen the demand and need for formal care inputs, as compared with an area where social relations are in a more fragmented state. Some elements contained within the grant-related expenditure assessment for local authorities[13] do attempt to take some account of such social conditions, but there is little evidence of well-researched and empirically based measures which can help the local service planner.

Resource allocation

Increasingly, service managers are involved in allocation decisions about how much support should be provided to individual informal carers. Such decisions may involve the provision of a paid member of staff to take over a task from an informal carer or to provide a period of respite care. The decision may involve indirect care provision through the use of vouchers which parents of handicapped children and others may use to 'buy' respite care from volunteers who have been vetted by a formal agency.

In all these cases, the issue for the manager of the service is how to control the open-endedness of the support. Which client should get a particular service and how frequently? How many vouchers is it appropriate to give an individual carer and to meet what needs? Such questions are probably only answerable in terms of comparisons with the level of commitment which would otherwise be required in providing more traditional services (as, for example in the Kent Community Care Project, where support to an elderly client living in the community can total up to two-thirds of the cost of a residential place).

A second problem for the resource allocator is how to compare the 'yield' from the input of staff time to the support of informal carers, through self-help and carers' groups, as against the benefits derived from using that time in direct input to needy clients/patients. How far can the 'multiplier' effect of support to carers be assessed? A parallel dilemma relates to investment in organisations supporting carers (often through joint finance) as against the commitment of resources to the enhancement of mainline services. The former option is less directly accountable and may raise fears of additional pressure on already over-stretched formal services. How far these can be compensated for by the potential indirect benefits provided through a voluntary organisation remains an open question.[14]

Economy, efficiency and effectiveness

It is clearly much easier to control an established formal service with clear management criteria and allocation rules than to respond to demands for a more flexible and responsive service. This has proved particularly true of initiatives such as family centres and mental health resource centres. Such services may appear to be less economic and less efficient, though they may in fact be more cost-effective. The service manager faces the difficulty of not being able to assess savings to formal services afforded by the input of informal carers caring for dependent relatives, nor the costs where such carers break down and are no longer able to care.

Developing a more flexible service outside the mainline statutory services, using paid carers or volunteers, needs an initial input of significant management attention to issues such as new systems and procedures for vetting workers, arranging about tax assessments where carers are paid, and arrangements for insurance and financial monitoring. These all constitute a significant overhead to the busy manager. Established national voluntary organisations such as the Crossroads Care Attendant Scheme, with a ready developed model of work and accountability, clearly have much to offer in these circumstances.

Improving services: a checklist for action

The following suggestions are put forward for statutory agencies to consider in their planning in order to ensure that greater support from formal sources is made available to informal carers. Ideally the agencies' aims should be that the person cared for receives the optimum service, the carer is adequately supported and relieved and the agency/agencies involved provide an equitable and effective service to both.

Information on the services available for different need groups in the community must be widely published, for professional staff use, for voluntary organisations providing advice and for those caring for those in need.[15] The implementation of Section 9 of the Disabled Persons (Services, Consultation and Representation) Act 1986 will assist in this regard. The use of information technology should further assist, both within agencies and through public sources such as reference libraries, etc. Initiatives such as DIAL (Disabled Information Advice Line) and the DHSS benefits advisory service, accessible by telephone, are beginning to meet such needs in part. Better knowledge of each other's services is a key requirement.

The members of the primary healthcare team are probably the professionals most frequently in touch with carers and those cared for.[16] It is critical that these groups are made aware of the range of services available and the criteria for their allocation. They need to see themselves as having the task of integrating formal and informal care.

The growing input from both the National Health Service and social services department (SSD) professionals in training and supporting self-help groups and other support groups for carers needs further expansion. It is likely that this investment pays dividends overall, even if on occasion specific schemes may not prove entirely successful. Paying part-time or full-time workers to sustain and develop such groups through a grant mechanism, rather than providing support through paid employees of the NHS or SSD who have to add this skill and interest to other duties, may be a more effective method of enabling self-help and innovation.[17] Representatives of statutory agencies working on project management committees can ensure good communication and maximum benefits.

Professional staff may well need new training in new skills to ensure that the 'community development type' tasks involved in working with voluntary groups, self-help groups and informal carers are achieved effectively.

Service providers should be assisted with the task of investigating the views of service recipients (and of those who receive and subsequently decline continued service) within a client/carer-orientated model of service provision, so as to improve the quality of service and its responsiveness to client/carers' needs.

Whilst the case remains unproven, a more responsive and effective service may be achieved by more decentralised service models.

More financial resources should be made available direct to clients/patients and carers to purchase their own care. Whilst DHSS supplementary benefit is available for residential care without an assessment of 'need', financial support is much less easily available for remaining in the community. A detailed study of the financial costs of disability being completed by the Office of Population Censuses and Surveys for the government should help to identify how best to target such additional resources, and the extent of the need for them.

Notes and References

1 Parker, G (1985), *With Due Care and Attention*, London, Family Policy Studies Centre and Willmott, P (1986), *Social Care Networks and Public Policy*, London, Policy Studies Institute.

2 Abrams, P (1978), 'Community Care – Some Research Problems and Priorities', in Barnes, J and Connelly, M (eds), *Social Care Research*, London, Bedford Square Press.

3 Challis, D and Davies, B (1987), *Case Management in Community Care*, London, Gower.

4 Black, J; Bowl, R; Burns, D; Critcher, C; Grant, G; Stockford, R (1983), *Social Work in Context*, London, Tavistock.

Hadley, R and McGrath, M (1984), *When Social Services are Local*, London, George Allen and Unwin.

Bayley, M; Seyd, R; Simons, K; Tennant, A (1985), *Neighbourhood Services Project, Dinnington: The Final Report*, University of Sheffield.

Hunt, A (1978), *The Elderly at Home*, London, HMSO.

Tinker, A (1984), *Staying at Home*, London, HMSO.

Wenger, G C (1984), *The Supportive Network*, London, George Allen and Unwin.

Sinclair, I; Crosbie, D; O'Connor, P; Stanforth, L; Vickery, A (1984) *Networks Project: A Study of Informal Care, Services and Social Work for Elderly Clients Living Alone*, London, National Institute for Social Work.

Levin, E; Sinclair, I; Gorbach, P (1983), *The Supporters of Confused Elderly People*, London, National Institute for Social Work.

Bayley, M (1973), *Mental Handicap and Community Care*, London, Routledge and Kegan Paul.

Glendinning, C (1983), *Unshared Care: Parents and Their Disabled Children*, London, Routledge and Kegan Paul.

Hatch, S and Hinton, T (1986), *Self-Help in Practice: A Study of Contact a Family, Community Work and Family Support*, University of Sheffield Joint Unit for Social Services Research.

Vaughn, C and Leff, J (1976) 'The Influence of Family and Social Factors on the Course of Psychiatric Illness', in *British Journal of Psychiatry* 129, pp 125–37.

Grad, J and Sainsbury, P (1968), 'The Effects That Patients Have on Their Families', in *British Journal of Psychiatry* 114.

Allen, I (1983), *Short-stay Residential Care for the Elderly*, London, Policy Studies Institute.

Carter, J (1981), *Day Services for Adults*, London, George Allen and Unwin.

Robinson, C (1986), *Avon Short-term Respite Care Scheme*, University of Bristol Department of Mental Health.

Stalker, K (1986), *Sharing Care*, University of Edinburgh Department of Social Administration.

Challis, D and Davies, B (1986), *Case Management in Community Care*, London, Gower.

Thornton, P and Moore, J (1980), *The Placement of Elderly People in*

Private Households, University of Leeds Department of Social Policy and Administration.

Abrams, P; Abrams, S; Humphrey, R; Snaith, R (1981), *Action for Care: a Review of Good Neighbour Schemes*, Berkhamsted, Volunteer Centre.

Bristow, A K (1981), *Crossroads Care Attendant Schemes*, Rugby, Association of Crossroads Care Attendant Schemes Ltd.

Maitland, N and Tutt, N (1987) 'Bexley's Trump Card' in *Social Services Insight*, 18 September 1987, pp 16-17.

Hatch, S and Hinton, T (1986), *Self-help in Practice: a Study of Contact a Family, Community Work and Family Support*, University of Sheffield Joint Unit for Social Services Research.

Vincent, J (1986), *Constraints on the Stability and Longevity of Self-help Groups in the Field of Health Care*, University of Loughborough Centre for Research in Social Policy.

5   See for example Briggs, A and Oliver, J (1985), *Caring: Experiences of Looking after Disabled Relatives*, London, Routledge and Kegan Paul.

6   Osborne, P (1987), 'Crossroads: Reaching Out and Meeting Needs' in *Community Care* supplement 'Inside respite care' 28 May 1987.

7   Payne, M (1986), *Social Care in the Community*, London, Macmillan.

8   Hadley, R and McGrath, M (1984), *When Social Services are Local*, London, George Allen and Unwin.

Bayley, M et al (1985), *Neighbourhood Services Project Dinnington Paper 12*, University of Sheffield Department of Sociological Studies.

9   Beresford, P and Croft, S (1986), *Whose Welfare?*, Brighton Polytechnic Urban Studies Centre.

10   Sinclair, I et al (1984), *op cit.*

11   Studies being undertaken by Gillian Daley, Development Worker, Primary Care Group, Kings Fund Centre, London. See Daley, G (1987), 'Decentralisation: a New way of Organising Community Health Services' in *Hospital and Health Services Review*, March 1987, pp 72-4. Also *Patching - in* (a newsletter for managers who are 'going local') available from the Kings Fund Centre, London.

12   *See* for example two articles on Gateshead Social Services Department's home care scheme: Snaith, R (1987) 'A More Responsive Approach' in *Community Care*, 18 June 1987, pp 16-17 and 'Coping with Problems and Policies' in *Community Care*, 25 June 1987, pp 24-26.

13   Details of factors included in the English GRE assessment formulae for personal social services can be found in Department of the Environment (1986), *Rate Support Grant England 1986/7*, London, HMSO.

14   Dr Eric Miller of the Tavistock Institute of Human Relations is currently evaluating a project funded by the DHSS under its 'Helping the Community to Care' initiative involving development officers working with self-help groups under the management of the Self-Help Alliance. Vincent, J (1986), *op cit* also provides some evidence and discussion of the relationships between self-help groups and support from formal caring agencies.

15   A recent initiative funded by the DHSS involved the wide circulation of a booklet prepared by the Kings Fund Informal Caring Support Unit explaining the variety of possible sources of respite care for carers.

16   See for example OPCS (1982), *The General Household Survey 1980*, London, HMSO. Tables 10.39–10.42 reveal that elderly people living at home see their GPs far more frequently than they receive any service from social services departments.

17   *See* for example Hatch, S and Hinton, T (1986) *op cit*; an account of a joint funded project focusing on the needs of carers by Sutton SSD and Merton and Sutton Health Authority in Benson, S (1987) 'Caring for the Carers', *Community Care*, 11 June 1987, pp 25–7 and an account of the KIDS family support project in Hampstead for families of disabled children in Mitchison, A (1987) 'Coping with a Disabled Child', *New Society*, 1 May 1987, p 29.

3 Conflict and collaboration: a study of voluntary organisations

Robert Nisbet

Looking back on those years before Glebe House, I'm not sure how we coped – well in truth, I don't think we did, we just existed, as sad and pathetic people, with this screaming child who was described as being mentally handicapped. (Mrs S, parent member, Charnwood Mencap Society)

This chapter is Mrs S's story. A story of how it feels to care, day in, day out, for a child with a mental handicap, and her quest for the improvement in the quality of her child's life as well as in the parents own. Sadly, it is the story of many parents of handicapped children. Their 'vision' was quite simple: a service that would provide them with some respite from the traumas of coping with a handicapped child. A respite which Mrs S wanted:

> when you want it, and not when you are told it's your turn, or 15 miles away in an isolated, run-down building. The dream of having some time to yourself, for your husband, for your other children – to feel that you can do what you want, when you want – simply to find some pleasure in life and not feel so guilty all the time. Yes, to have a direct say over what care is to be provided.

To many families with a mentally handicapped member, the range and extent of services provided by numerous agencies is often confusing and perceived as being quite remote from many of their everyday problems and concerns. The question of whom they should approach, and for what service, is beset with concerns as to whether they have contacted the right agency or indeed the right professional within that agency. Most important are the issues of how their needs will be interpreted, and the acceptance or otherwise of their own views as the principal carers.

Attending a fairly typical case conference on an adolescent currently at a special school, but soon to move to a social services day centre, highlights the baffling complexities and interpretations when young adults' needs are prescribed by no less than three separate and distinct agencies (health, education and social services), each with different responsibilities and requirements for service provision. In turn these agencies can be represented often by no fewer than eight to twelve different professionals, all of whom may have varying backgrounds in terms of training, outlook, professional experience, and personal values and attitudes which can be brought to the forefront in influencing the destiny of the client. In addition it is often the case that the parents, with no preparatory training and little previous knowledge of the agencies and professionals with whom they consult, are required to place their trust and confidence impartially and with little opportunity for redress or continued involvement.

The Glebe House Project, a small project set up by a local Mencap society, offered the chance for a group of parents to design and manage their own services from one central point. The service, they anticipated, would meet many of their needs, and work towards a closer integration of all services in the area.

This project demonstrates some of the means of integrating local services and, moreover, the development of a closer partnership between carers. In terms of its achievement of these goals, the process has not always been easy, and indeed the 'integration' of services has come by means of pressure and often as a consequence of fierce and protracted negotiation.

A case study of the Glebe House Project shows how certain principles and approaches have been used with great effect in helping people with a mental handicap, and their families, to achieve a more comprehensive and integrated service. The project attempts to break down barriers between agencies by ensuring that all concerned work towards common objectives in the provision of services. In the establishment of these objectives, emphasis is placed upon the involvement of parents and/or other carers, and people with a handicap themselves.

As a case study of a local project it illustrates the particular influences — political, cultural and economic — that any local community may give rise to in its history. Certain peculiarities, distinct in some ways and yet entwined with social and economic policy directives, make it unique and separate from other local communities' experiences and likely development.

This is a tale of a group of parents who decided to promote their own services to the exclusion and initial annoyance of the statutory services in the area. From this early independence, there then arose the need to secure long-term finances and hence the need for greater collaboration and integration with the statutory services.

The case study is one which demonstrates an uneasiness of relationship between a statutory and a voluntary sector, and concludes that this will always remain where power, expertise and bureaucratisation is very unevenly distributed. We see the struggle between an isolated group of parents creating their 'vision' of community care, and finding that this in essence conflicted with the more established format of the same policy in the area. Yet this conflict in the end resulted in a positive outcome, in the bringing together of service departments to provide a service for the consumer that was both more integrated and responsive, and one that essentially involved the consumer in its making.

Background to the project

The Glebe House Project in Loughborough was established by the Charnwood Mencap Society in mid-1983. Its overall aim is to provide a comprehensive and integrated system of support services for families and their mentally handicapped members, based at one central location.

Glebe House, a former Victorian rectory, is situated a short distance from the town centre, near the University campus and a pleasant residential area. The Society rents the property from the Leicestershire Education Committee, who previously used the building as a teachers' resource centre. Indeed, the grounds are currently shared with a junior school.

Renovations of the property were undertaken by the Society with assistance from a Department of the Environment grant and a small revenue grant towards the House's running costs was secured from the county council's Urban Policies Sub-Committee.

Before the Glebe House Project was created, little distinguished Charnwood Mencap Society from many of the other local societies affiliated to National Mencap. Over its 20 years' history, it had raised money and contributed to the services provided by the statutory sector in terms of equipment purchase and payments for holidays. Many key professionals (eg head teacher, day centre manager) served on the executive committee, with meetings being held in the statutory service's premises. Minutes of the executive's meetings for those years bear witness to the role of professionals advising and dominating the forum, with little opportunity for parents to hold the statutory sector to account and so influence changes in the way those services were being provided. Criticism of services was guarded, whilst professionals believed themselves to be carrying out a crucial liaison role. There was essentially compliance to the professionals' agendas, with virtual assimilation of the Society into the statutory sector's network of services. No other forums in the area existed through which parents could voice their views.

Parents expressed many frustrations as to the lack of support they received from the existing services and, moreover, to their location and availability. At the time the key issue stemmed from the following factors:

1   Residential care was located considerable distances from the families in the area – resulting in long travelling times, disruption and stress for the individuals involved. Residential care was specifically provided in 25-place bedded hostels, or hospitals.

2   Short-term care had to be booked months in advance. Crises were dealt with on the basis of wherever there was a bed available, rather than on an assessment of an individual's need and preferences.

3   The day centre served a large catchment area, with resulting complex and frustrating transport problems. Like the residential service, day care was managed centrally at County Hall, and had no formal links or local representation with its users or their families.

4   For adults with profound and multiple handicaps no social service provision was available: hospital services were located some distance away, and were strongly criticised for their inadequacies and inappropriateness by many families.

5   No regular social work support was available, and very few social workers in the area had any interest in mental handicap. No social workers at the time had any specialist responsibility. Likewise, community and paramedical services in the area were either remote or non-existent.

6   No formal liaison existed between the families and the statutory services, through which needs could be identified and solutions sought. The local Mencap Society was not perceived by its members as having this role.

7   The local special school, whilst centrally placed in the community, had antagonised several parents, specifically over their perceived lack of involvement in the running of the school. As a result, the parents-teachers association was disbanded.

Evolution into a pressure group activity was slow but, by 1982, the dissatisfaction with the statutory services, expressed in particular by the more articulate parent members, reached the point where they held a number of meetings called 'Survival'.

The meetings, which excluded professionals, were open to parents and relatives only, to encourage freedom of expression. Groups were formed with the task of defining the support services which they really needed, and of assigning priorities to their suggestions.

The harsh picture of the high costs of caring for carers emerged from those meetings, and is consistent with a growing body of evidence highlighting the physical, emotional and social strains of caring, particularly for women. Most caring is carried out by women.

The choices facing most women were either being overburdened with paid work and caring, or caring and not being employed, with all the attached social and economic disadvantages.

Essentially, the carers at these meetings called for practical help (Charnwood Mencap 1982), including:

1 Help in the home.
2 Care for children during the long school holidays (summer holidays in Leicestershire schools are between 8 and 9 weeks).
3 Information and advice orientated to the needs of carers rather than to those of professionals.
4 Respite care, particularly for the more severely handicapped adults, as an alternative to hospital – and a locally provided service.
5 Emergency help and support at times of crisis.

Concerning this support, the parents had some very real problems:

> Lack of information was a very general complaint at the meeting. Many people were surprised to learn important facts about available services from others present and were angry that they had not been informed officially. Social workers were generally regarded as unreliable sources of information about mental handicap. Most people present felt that they had no-one to turn to who was on their side when they needed general advice, or support when complaining to the authorities. Some kind of advocate was needed for parents to do this effectively for us. It was agreed that the parents would have to organise this themselves possibly through the Society. (Charnwood Mencap 1982)

Such were the expressed needs of a fairly isolated group of parents. These were needs that central government has also argued as important: 'most carers require a "package" of care, combining financial benefits, counselling, respite care, domiciliary services, day care, short-stay residential care and other forms of support' (DHSS 1984).

Parents felt frustrated, rarely consulted and distanced geographically as well as professionally from existing services – services they perceived as being poor in quality and generally to be used only as a 'last resort'.

Whilst such analysis of needs and consensus of views held by a group of parents could have been used to pressurise the statutory sector services, it was agreed through the Mencap Society's executive committee to establish and manage their own localised set of services. They knew what they needed; the expertise was vested in them as parents and carers – 'the customer', they declared, 'is right' (Meddis 1985). Furthermore the project represented, most significantly, an approach that could cut across the statutory boundaries. Parents spoke of the confusion, duplication, shortfalls and conflicts caused by having a range of services provided by so many bureaucratic and large organisations.

Going it alone — developing services

The first services commenced in June 1983, through funding from the Manpower Services Commission (MSC) under the Community Programme. This enabled the short-term employment of 27 staff, the majority of whom were part-time. Services initially offered were a summer holiday playscheme, a Saturday morning shoppers' creche, and an information service combining welfare rights, a domiciliary home care and sitting-in service. Later in the first year of the project, a pre-school playgroup, adult day care and occasional weekend respite care were initiated.

The project was formally opened by Brian Rix, National Mencap's Director General, in October 1983. National media reportage was focused on the project when HRH The Princess of Wales visited the project in April 1984 to meet the parents, their children and staff. Apart from the publicity, the event gained the project considerable prestige and standing in the local community.

A few months later, however, the project's Community Pro-gramme staff group was reduced to 19 places, following a reduction of the Community Programme in the area. At the same time, following some administrative and managerial difficulties within the project itself, the financial management of the MSC project was taken over by the Charnwood Borough Council's Community Programme agency. Staff within particular sectors of the project (ie home care, under 5s playgroup) were kept on, using bridging finance from the health authority.

During this time, difficult and protracted negotiations were being undertaken for the financial support of the entire project from joint finance. For reasons to be returned to later, the social service department's management opposed all but a small part of the project. Their objections seemed focused on the cost implications of supporting several services requiring a fairly large building. Support was forthcoming from various political quarters and departments at County Hall, however, as well as from the health authority. The lack of corporate policy as to how the project should be approached enabled certain components of the scheme to be supported, and social service's views undermined.

In November 1984 agreement was reached by the joint consultative committee (JCC) to support the home care service, and under 3s opportunity group. At the JCC meeting, the hope was expressed by members and officers that in future voluntary organisations might take steps to assure themselves of the availability of medium- and long-term finance before embarking on a project, especially a substantial project for which only short-term finance was initially available.

In addition, the JCC took the general view that although the project was presented as a three-year pilot project, it would not be realistic to regard it as anything other than one which Charnwood Mencap would expect to be continued beyond the three-year period. The JCC also had to pay regard to the limited amount of joint finance available in the next few years and the need to ensure that there would be sufficient joint finance remaining uncommitted to enable new projects, both voluntary and statutory, to be approved for joint finance during those years.

From the parents' perspective, they did not feel adequate forums existed through which their needs could be expressed and listened to. Further, their perception of the statutory services was such that convinced them that 'going it alone' would be the only way they could adequately meet their needs on their terms. The risk of using short-term finance was obvious and critical, but it did at least raise the profile of their views and, as we shall see, their inclusion as partners in service provision. The argument of the lack of availability of resources was questioned by parents who saw additional hostels and day centres being built, without regard to the local community's views or, most importantly, the views of their appropriateness or otherwise by consumers themselves. Money would and could be found if there was involvement and commitment by officers and professionals of the statutory services. The task then began of gaining that commitment and involvement.

Gaining commitment and involvement in partnership

Given the history of the project, developing through short-term means and without consultation and prior approval by some of the key statutory services, how has the project moved forward towards a more integrated approach?

In particular, three forums have been created by the project with the aim of establishing better understanding between agencies, their professional practitioners and service managers. Most importantly, the forums have served to involve the users, or their representatives, in the process of establishing their needs clearly and how, from a range of resources and services, these may be met.

The Practitioners' Group

This quarterly meeting enables key practitioners from the project, social services, education and health authorities who work in the area, to meet, share concerns, coordinate inputs, avoid duplication and create a better understanding and harmony between the services.

Such an example has been the provision of two playgroups for children under three being promoted by both the local special school and the project itself. Apart from the ineffective use of resources, anxieties were being expressed by parents that if they did not send their child to the school's playgroup they feared the disqualification of their child from an early admission to school. Through the Practitioners' Group this issue was raised, enabling an agreement to be reached as to how the service was to be provided so as to avoid duplication. Other concerns, such as holiday playscheme catchment areas, sharing facilities and equipment, have been raised and resolved.

The Policy Group

Many concerns raised by the practitioners, and indeed ideas for the improvement of services, are debated at a 'Policy Group' which is made up of executive members of the Society, the project manager, and senior managers from social services, health authority and education department. The aim of this Group is similar to that of the Practitioners' Group – to facilitate closer collaboration, and integration of the various services. Whilst the potential exists for a better understanding, unfortunately the quantum leap in imagination to effect better sharing and communication has not always matched the principles underlying the Group. Both groups have been administered by the project itself, and whilst the statutory agencies have been supportive of the forums, there has been felt to be a reluctance to give them a sense of clear definition and authority in their role. Certainly, they broke down barriers of the 'empires', for those that chose to be active in them.

Programme planning meetings

A move towards integrating the care systems in the area and a better coordination of services had to be achieved if the project was to survive. Enabling other agencies to be involved practically in the project became a requirement in order for the project to be perceived as being of benefit to professionals in their day-to-day practice. Offering a process with some structure behind it can provide security. It can also aid communication and resolve misunderstandings. Most importantly, the introduction of programme planning meetings was seen as the means through which support and encouragement could be given to those people who usually have least opportunity to develop and express their views about what should happen: parents, care staff and people with mental handicaps themselves.

Whilst it is difficult to measure or monitor accurately the success of the introduction of programme planning in bringing more security to the project, it is anticipated that this will achieve involvement, coordination and the sharing of resources (and often expertise), as well as moving to a more realistic and practical basis of partnership. Programme planning became the main and essential meeting ground for users of the project, both from the families' and professionals' perspective. Professionals and their agencies became involved not as authoritative figures or principally as gatekeepers, but as partners and equals with parents. Professionals were valued for their expertise, commitment and specialist knowledge, not for their agency authority.

As one parent put it:

> I felt I could come to Glebe House and sit down and talk about my concerns for my daughter in a relaxed way. The people there genuinely wanted to help me – they all went to great trouble to listen to my point of view – I felt very important and understood. Towards the end we talked about what should happen – I was very surprised . . . . I thought they would ask me to leave the room at this point – but they didn't, we all left together!.

Statutory agencies still represent a major contribution to the overall service provision for families in the area. People with a mental handicap spend a considerable proportion of their lives in some aspect of the formal care and educational system, be it at school, day centre or, for a small but nevertheless significant number, in some form of residential provision. As such, the involvement and views of these services could not be considered in isolation from the day-to-day services of the Glebe House Project and its future development.

At the time of the instigation of the Glebe House Project, no systematic review, strategy or collective forum for the coordination of support and services existed. Opportunities such as school medicals and 'crisis' case conferences served to emphasise the power of professionals and their key roles as decision-makers and gatekeepers. This largely excluded or discounted views of parents and, most significantly, the individuals themselves.

Younger parents contrasted these forums to that of the service provided to them under the local Portage Scheme that operated for pre-school Downs Syndrome children. This was a service which involved them at every step.

Agencies found it particularly difficult to listen to or value each other's contribution: hence the atmosphere of misunderstanding. By sharing perceptions and by recognising the importance of parents' views with equal status to that of professionals, integration of care can become a reality, though it should not deny or assimilate the individuality of those who make up the partnership.

Evaluation

Unfortunately, the Glebe House Project did not achieve this equity in its working role with other agencies – the potential, though, was there, undermined by the considerable inequitable distribution of resources and power. Programme planning demonstrated the possibility of closer partnership and of greater resource and power sharing. Inequity will always undermine any sense of genuine and long-term partnership.

Moves, however, from the statutory services towards a more integrated service, came in particular from the specialist social worker's role. Specialist workers for people with mental handicap became employed by the social services department from mid-1985. In a move towards the establishment of a community-based mental handicap service, the health authority envisaged the setting up of local Community Mental Handicap Teams. As part of that programme, several specialist social work posts were supported, including two for the area served by Glebe House. The third area covered by the project already had a specialist social worker, through an internal reorganisation.

Overall, the involvement of the specialists had a clear influence in moving services in the area to a more integrated approach. Their direct and regular involvement with families firstly helped change many parents' perceptions of social workers to a more positive one (a perception also portrayed by Glebe House), and secondly assisted them to use the range of services more effectively to meet their needs.

Writing in the Charnwood Mencap Society's *Annual Yearbook* for 1985, the Area Social Services Director commented:

> It is with some gratification that the two groups which meet at Glebe House have flourished over the last year with both the Policy Group and the Practitioners' Group beginning to evolve as an important focus for coordinating the activities of the statutory and voluntary agencies.

Their report concluded by adding:

> Looking ahead to the New Year, the new appointments [of specialist social workers] and the consolidation and development which can be expected with the new Divisions, will offer greater opportunities for cooperation and coordination of services.

Lessons learned

What had mitigated against planned collaboration and integration in this case example?

There is a sense that the statutory services in the area had a different perception of what needs existed and how they should be met. There is, underlying all this, a philosophical misconception by professionals that when parents and other principal carers highlight the great burden of care, that this can be interpreted as not wishing to continue caring, when really the difficulties arise and reach breaking point when there is a lack of choice, involvement and appropriate forms of practical support available to carers.

Finch (1985) has argued the importance of policies which take such 'emotions and affections more seriously' – releasing relatives and friends to offer more personal warmth and affection 'by removing the fear of becoming entangled in pressures to provide domestic and nursing care'.

The approach of statutory authorities can appear remote, reactive to crises, and seemingly unresponsive to the everyday toil of the carer's world. Planning of services has traditionally been based on 'bricks and mortar': adding more of the same to the existing stock. In this incremental process, the authorities rarely consulted their consumers to find out how they saw the services and the changes required in them.

Fundamental concerns in the lack of information were typified by the parent members of Charnwood Mencap Society, who at their meetings spoke of:

> a great desire for more information concerning the running of the day centre on such topics as (i) education, (ii) policy and structure of the centre, (iii) conditions of work for the trainees, (iv) basis on which payments are made to members.

At the time no advisory consultative group involving users or parents was in operation – and this state of affairs was commonplace in the authority.

Services remote from their principal users, or indeed those whose interests they claim to uphold, must not be surprised by the differences in views held by services and users regarding what needs exist and by what means they should be met. Perhaps parents in the Society needed to have used existing structures more forthrightly to bring about change within the agencies rather than to have gone it alone!

A further concern that proved a barrier to the integration of services arose from the policy, unwritten but nevertheless dominant in its influence, of the demarcation of services. Who should provide what service, for whom and where? The division of responsibilities between the education department and the health and social services agencies were blurred and temperamental. At its worst, the social services made it quite clear in its provision that they would accept no long-term responsibility for the profoundly handicapped apart from a minimal day care service. This became a specific issue of concern for the parents' group. For the health authority's part, it was, in 1983, planning a strategy of service provision for the next ten years. The closure of hospitals was imminent, but little consultation was taking place as to how services should be developed and deployed in the community. Indeed, such key initiative money as joint finance was being used to enable the local authority to increase its own hostel and day care services. Planning for these hostel and day centres had been carried out prior to local authority expenditure cuts, and were now 'resuscitated' to take up the offer from joint finance. Within these facilities little consideration was given to the needs of profoundly handicapped people. With expenditure committed to these projects, the local authority could 'justly' argue that it had little capacity to take up further joint financed projects – particularly those from the voluntary sector.

A further issue, concerning how support services for families can be met, appears around the role that is typically identified for community associations and voluntary service agencies in the development of informal networks of care and support. From this follows the assumption that there is a vast untapped army of potential volunteers, freely provided to supplement statutory service provision. This is a concept vividly described by Abrams (1984):

> To put it melodramatically, the possibility of community care represents an alternative to the surrender of social responsibility to officials .... The underlying assumption seems to be that the home and the family should, whenever possible, be the immediate setting and agency for care and that the task of procuring care is centrally one of building up the ability and willingness of families to accept this role.

Most parents in the Society were the strongest advocates of wishing to continue caring for their 'dependent' relative at home. How their 'willingness' and 'ability' was to be strengthened became the crucial issue of conflict between the statutory agencies and the parents' group. The parents were wishing to promote and control their own services to run alongside other statutory and traditional resources. The statutory services, for their part, would have preferred a more volunteer-orientated initiative directed and, indeed, based within their own services in the area.

Afterthoughts

This case study demonstrates some of the problems and issues surrounding a pluralistic approach to providing localised services. In an attempt to provide key practical services from one centre and to match services provided in the area by other agencies, the project met quite considerable opposition and competition for funding.

Without a clear and long-term strategy for funding the voluntary sector on an equitable basis to their statutory partners, any moves towards collaboration will always have a competitive and damaging element. The perceptions each sector has of the other need careful analysis and testing – in order for common ground to be found.

Integration should not mean assimilation. It must recognise the status of parents as potential partners in the provision of care – as well as valuing the unique and individual perspective, skills and experience that they can bring to the process. The achievement of this on an equitable basis is paramount – regardless of the changes that this may bring to the established and traditional formats of planning and decision-making. Services must arise from the concerns and needs of their potential users and, further, the users' continued involvement must remain of principal concern and influence in the daily practice of statutory agencies and their professional staff groups.

References

Charnwood Mencap Society (1982) '*Survival – Report to Members of Charnwood Mencap Society of the meeting to discuss Problems Faced by Families with a Mentally Handicapped Dependent*' June/July 1982 – Charnwood Mencap Society.

DHSS (1984) '*Supporting the Informal Carers: Fifty Styles of Caring, Models of Practice for Planners and Practitioners*' Social Work Service Development Group Project Report, p 6.

Meddis, R (1985) 'Local Support Services for the Mentally Handicapped'. The British Psychological Society, Division of Clinical Psychology Newsletter, no 49, September 1985, pp 31–35.

Charnwood Mencap Society (1985) *Annual Year Book 1985/86*, 'The Glebe House Project: Social Services Perspective of Services for Mentally Handicapped People'. Charnwood Mencap Society.

Finch, J (1985) A response to Robert Harris, 'End Points and Starting Points'. *Critical Social Policy* issue 12, spring 1985, pp 115–122.

See also Finch, J (1984) Community Care: Developing Non-Sexist Alternatives. *Critical Social Policy*, issue 9, spring 1984, pp 6–18, pp 11–12.

Abrams, P (1984) Martin Balmer (ed), 'Realistics of Neighbourhood Care: The Interactions between Statutory, Voluntary and Informal Social Care', *Policy and Politics*, 12(4), pp 413–29.

4 Linking housing and care

Malcolm Cooper

Any conviction which may be discerned from the following few pages springs from hard experience. In order to deliver a rational and efficient service to the community, professionals must learn new skills and foster new attitudes. This chapter is written from the viewpoint of a housing professional who knows that trust, patience and good faith are the predominant qualities of service-providers in the age of care in the community.

Housing and care: the background

People in need of care in the community do not classify their needs into separate compartments. The need for care is experienced as an entity. It may seem all the more strange, therefore, that the provision of care to meet these needs is divided between various agencies. The complex of central and local government agencies and voluntary bodies which may converge on a single person in need may seem daunting and incomprehensible. Indeed, the complexity of service delivery is such that some people in need may be deterred from seeking assistance. We see this in other connections too, for example in the fact that many low-income households do not apply for the financial benefits to which they are entitled.

The diversity of the ways we support people in need runs through all levels of government. The provision of housing, the provision of care and the provision of financial support, to give but three examples, have traditionally been regarded as separate services with enabling powers contained in completely different legislation. Whilst the Housing Acts confer certain powers and duties relating to the provision of housing accommodation, a variety of other legislation is relevant to the provisions of care, or of pensions, or of income support. From this separation of the various aspects of personal care and support at the source, divisions are perpetuated right down to the point of service delivery. So it is that the prime responsibility for housing and care resides in different government ministries. As the structure is traced downwards towards the point of provision, it is found that throughout the shire counties, housing is the responsibility of district councils, care is provided by the counties and income support by the local offices of central government ministries. Superimposed on this complex structure, housing associations and various voluntary organisations make many specialist contributions to particular groups in society.

Such complexity in the ways in which services are provided at the point of delivery is a matter of concern. Practitioners, however highly motivated to provide a rational and efficient service to the people they serve, find themselves in a 'cleft stick'. On the one hand, there is the temptation to provide their part of the overall service as efficiently as possible, and run the risk of being completely out of phase with what other bodies are doing. This can be wasteful. On the other hand, it may seem attractive to take steps to coordinate the delivery of services with the representatives of other locally active bodies, and run the risk of making very slow and expensive progress. The danger is that disillusionment can creep in if progress stemming from the work of committees and groups (which, inevitably, have to be set up) seems meagre and out of proportion to the resources which have to be deployed.

But why should district councils be directly involved in the provision of care? The reasons, together with recently published views of the Association of District Councils, which has examined this question, are now discussed.

Housing and care: why the services converge

It would be possible to maintain the view that it is neither intended nor necessary for housing authorities to become involved in the provision of care, but they are often both interested and very actively involved. This involvement springs from the powers and duties placed on housing authorities by the Housing Act 1985 and is greatest with the authority's own tenants. For whatever reasons – the sense of responsibility felt by many democratically elected councils will be one – housing authorities have shown a definite willingness to use the powers confirmed by statute to care for their own tenants.

There are at least four substantial considerations which converge to make the provision of care an issue for those who provide housing. These are given below.

The success of sheltered housing

The phrase 'sheltered housing' has become a technical term. It refers to housing developments in which accommodation, especially suitable for the elderly, is grouped together and supervised by a warden who, usually, lives on the scheme. The role of the warden is to be no more than a good neighbour figure to keep an eye on the tenants and respond quickly should any need arise. The basic assumption behind sheltered housing is that elderly people should be encouraged to live lives as independent as possible. Even with advancing years most are able to do this for most of the time. Indeed, it has been estimated that only 6% of elderly people do not live independently in their own homes. By living in sheltered groups with a warden on hand to provide support for those periods when, because of illness or some other reason, they cannot be totally independent, the elderly can be supported at home instead of moving to more supportive accommodation.

The appearance of sheltered housing has been one of the most significant developments in postwar housing. Perhaps not surprisingly, the concept has evolved further over the years. For example, sheltered housing schemes are now usually provided with various communal facilities such as a lounge with kitchen, laundry, guest bedroom and, almost without exception, an intercommunication system. With the advent of these developments has come increased scope for care and welfare.

By 1970, in response to government guidance, so-called Category II sheltered schemes began to appear. These were designed to be suitable for occupation by people who, whilst keeping their independence, required rather more support than could be provided easily in ordinary sheltered housing. Category II schemes are arranged in such a way that the front doors open out on to a heated corridor, rather than the outside environment, and all the dwellings are centrally heated.

Rather like the National Health Service, sheltered housing, by being a success, has inevitably led to increased demand for resources. There is evidence that elderly people living in sheltered housing live longer than others. Certainly, with the passage of time, the very large number of people now living successfully in sheltered schemes have grown older and relatively more dependent. This has given rise to a new development during the past 10 years or so: the specialised sheltered housing scheme which is sometimes referred to as Part 2½ housing. Housing authorities have felt obliged to offer the increased level of support available in such schemes to cope with the ever-increasing number of frail people among their tenants. Thus local authorities who used, mainly, to be concerned with the provision of accommodation for families, especially after the two world wars, have now built so many elderly persons' bungalows and flats that they have become deeply involved with this section of the community. Whilst the effect of the 'right to buy' has led to a reduction in the total local authority and housing association dwelling stock, the combined total of such properties is still something approaching five million. When one considers that, in some local authorities, elderly persons' grouped dwellings account for over 12% of the authority's housing stock, it becomes clear how extensive is the involvement of housing authorities in the lives of elderly people. It does not end there, however, because all housing authorities have a further substantial number of elderly households in accommodation outside sheltered housing schemes. For example, in a survey conducted by East Cambridgeshire District Council in 1982-3, it was found that over 47% of council dwelling households contained no-one under the age of 60. In 17% of the total households there was no-one under the age of 75.

With these statistics in mind, one may ask: where do housing responsibilities end and welfare responsibilities begin? Housing authorities employ thousands of wardens who live on the spot and are constantly asked or are tempted to play a caring role. It is surprising that, at the point of delivery, housing and welfare services converge?

Population trends

Those who accept that the provision of housing and the provision of care are unavoidably linked will be alerted by the projected increases in the population, especially for the very old, to the year 2001, published by the Office of Population Censuses and Surveys.

The impact of these projections will be the greater because of the

TABLE 4.1 Age structure of the population – United Kingdom (in millions)

	60–74	75–84	85+
1961	6.8	1.9	0.3
1971	8.0	2.2	0.5
1981	8.1	2.7	0.6
1986	8.1	3.0	0.7
1991	7.8	3.0	0.9
1996	7.6	3.0	1.0
2001	7.4	3.0	1.0

current policy of care in the community. The prospect of a million people over the age of 85, the majority of whom will be living in their own homes, will place increasing pressure on the resources of both housing and welfare authorities.

The care in the community policy

During the past few years, the government has introduced and implemented its care in the community policy. It is now accepted widely that a person confined to an institution for a long period of time gradually loses the ability to be independent. Institutional life is now seen as something to be avoided, if possible, in caring for people. The assumption has been voiced in some quarters that care in the community is easier on the public purse. In other quarters this assumption is met with scepticism.

The operation of this policy has resulted in significant numbers of people being cared for in the community, who previously might have entered institutions. More recently the policy has been extended to include the return to the community after careful preparation of many of those living in institutions. Housing authorities and housing associations have been caught up in the provision of homes for the people concerned, who inevitably need high levels of care.

One direct result of this policy has been to increase the number of dependent people occupying local authority dwellings, who might previously have moved into care institutions. Another is the steadily increasing level of provision of specialist housing for groups other than the elderly; for example, the mentally and physically handicapped. Looking to the future, another factor has come into view. The potential demands on the caring services posed by AIDS are being defined and redefined. The situation society will face in the future cannot be foreseen clearly but it seems likely that if the numbers of those affected become large, AIDS sufferers will be cared for and die at home because hospital space will simply not be available for all. Should that happen, the close involvement of housing authorities will be inescapable.

The effect of council house sales

The government has announced that over a million houses have been sold since 1980. This represents approximately 17% of the stock. As a result of this development there are clear indications that, of those who remain as tenants, a higher proportion than previously are in rent arrears, receive housing benefit, are elderly or have other specialised needs. This development tends to accentuate the element of care in the provision of housing. It may also have contributed to a noticeable increase in the numbers of people registering on housing waiting lists and presenting themselves as homeless. In trying to meet the needs of vulnerable people who are without adequate housing accommodation, housing authorities will inevitably become involved in elements of care.

Four of the factors which have further blurred the indistinct line dividing housing and care have been described. In view of this, what should be the respective responsibilities and involvement of housing and welfare authorities? An increased awareness of this issue has, with the assistance of government guidelines, led to a closer examination of the need for cooperation and joint planning between health, social services and housing authorities together with the voluntary sector.

The Association of District Councils, a body which represents the interests of 333 non-metropolitan district councils throughout England and Wales, published a review of housing policies in March 1987 entitled *Foundations for Future Housing*. Some of its conclusions indicate the extent to which the issues relating to the provision of services in the community were considered. For example:

Conclusion 50 — Local authorities should consider the provision of community and social facilities as an inseparable part of their housing role.

Conclusion 51 — The Association draws attention to the increasing involvement of district councils in providing special care for tenants; particularly for the increased proportion of elderly in council housing.

Conclusion 52 — The Association readily accepts this extended responsibility implied by 'care in the community' and indeed considers that residential accommodation administered by county councils should also be transferred to housing authorities.

Conclusion 53 — The Association supports cooperation with other agencies involved in providing for the elderly and disabled through joint planning and provision and welcomes the recent initiative by the Audit Commission in making suggestions for improvement to the present somewhat cumbersome machinery.

Conclusion 54 — Resources, including bridging finance, are a key element in providing community care and must be increased.

The case has been made. A division of responsibility for the delivery of housing and welfare services cannot be easily justified. Care in the community has a further dimension and that is medical care. How can the various strands of the service to be delivered to the person at home be drawn together?

Housing and care: advice, accountability and cooperation

For the reasons discussed above, there is ample justification for stressing one or two consequences of care in the community. Its impact will be different for each agency concerned with providing it. Its effect on the recipient may be daunting. Housing authorities will be drawn into the sphere of care more and more, as a result of the increasing number of dependent people in the community. The recipient of care at home may be confused as he or she attempts to understand which statutory or voluntary agency is appropriate. We are facing a situation in which millions of people growing steadily less confident in themselves, needing advice or support in an increasing number of areas, confront a world in which the services they need are provided by a variety of different agencies served by different people in different offices. It is a recipe for confusion at the very least.

If people in the numbers envisaged are to be cared for at home then three elements are thrown into relief and require discussion. They are advice, accountability and cooperation.

Advice

The noticeable increase in the provision of advice in society, as evidenced by the growth in Citizens Advice Bureaux and Housing Advice Centres, is indication enough of people's need for easy access to reliable information. If dependent people are to be enabled to remain and be cared for in their own homes, then they must be given good information and advice about the care or help they need. For example, in 1983 East Cambridgeshire District Council realised that many of the elderly people applying for sheltered accommodation really preferred to stay where they were in their homes, surrounded by the memories of a lifetime. Their reasons for wanting a move varied but included such factors as anxiety about money and the cost of maintaining the house, the unsuitability of the dwelling and the need for help in emergencies.

The Council's response was to appoint an Elderly Persons' Adviser. This person has enough knowledge about matters such as housing benefits, DHSS income support, repairs grants, mortgage and other finance, intercommunication systems, the care services and alternative types of accommodation, to help elderly people review all the options before committing themselves to a move.

In fact what was created was a sort of 'one-stop shopping' facility which immediately overcame most of the difficulties caused by the divisions of the care services. The demand for the service offered, and the fact that so many other housing authorities have followed suit, is evidence enough that the provision of care in the community is greatly helped by a 'one-stop' advice service.

Accountability

The underlying theme of this chapter has been the tension between a single client who may have a range of needs, and society at large which meets those needs by offering a range of, often unconnected, specialist services. An advice service may help to overcome the confusion in the recipient's mind, but the services themselves remain unconnected and the providers answerable to different masters. There is, therefore, the need to address the question of account-ability. That is answered relatively easily if the different services continue to be delivered each by its responsible agency without reference to the others. In such a situation, housing authorities would be accountable for housing, social services authorities for welfare and so on. But care in the community forces attention to the need to rationalise and coordinate the delivery of services. Once different authorities start to consider a measure of joint action in the interests of greater efficiency, then the question of accountability comes into focus.

What is obvious is that one authority in such a joint venture cannot be made accountable for another authority's contribution. In practice we find that this principle is seen most clearly when applied to the control of staff and budgets.

Let us suppose, therefore, that the various agencies concerned in a particular area with the delivery of care services resolve to try and coordinate their individual contributions. What are their options? Three come readily to mind:

1 Informal cooperation – where sufficient goodwill, trust and understanding exist between the members and officers of the different agencies, each may continue to be separately account-able for its own element of the overall service, but this is delivered in a way which is sensitive and responsive to the work of the others.
2 Implementation groups – where a task is sufficiently distinct, for example the rehousing in the community of a given group of mentally handicapped people, then the various authorities may choose to set up a separate inter-agency group. In the example given, representatives of housing, social services, the health authority and voluntary sector may formally constitute such an

implementation group. The group would have a leader who would be accountable to all the constituent agencies for the achievement of the task. The group would control the budget after it had been funded and agreed by the agencies concerned.

3   The lead authority – it may be that the contribution of one authority is to be far greater than the others. In such a situation the lesser partners may agree to place their resources in the hands of a lead authority and, with it, accountability.

Cooperation

The needs of the people we serve demand cooperation between the caring agencies. Those who have had experience of joint ventures, and have started to explore the various ways of working together with other agencies to deliver care services in the community, have learnt valuable lessons. Perhaps the most important is that old attitudes to work have to change; new skills are required. The single-mindedness and dedication which typified the committed professional in the past are now not enough. Cooperation, to work smoothly, requires people who are both professionally competent in their own fields and also do not find it difficult to trust others over whom they have no direct control. They will require more than a fair share of patience and understanding. They must be disciplined, always able to do exactly what it is agreed they should do as part of the joint scheme of things. To do otherwise leads to a strain in working relationships and to motives being questioned.

For these reasons cooperative working is harder than single agency working and it calls for an investment in training and a new breed of manager. But that is not all, for there can sometimes emerge another difficulty, which is that groups which lack sufficient commitment, leadership or experience may spend so much time sparring in committee that insufficient time and energy remain actually to deliver the service.

Delivering the service: some examples

Preferences about the best way to proceed in planning and delivering services jointly may vary. Within the Cambridge Health Authority Area, which encompasses three district councils, various successful ventures have taken place. In the three examples described below events were managed by a joint implementation group.

Bedford House, Ely

The proposals provide for the conversion of a handsome Georgian house in the centre of Ely and the redevelopment of the land associated with it to provide the following accommodation:

— 25 unsupervised flats for independent elderly people;
— a 26-place specialised sheltered housing scheme for frail elderly people;
— an eight-place unit for elderly, mentally infirm people;
— five flats on upper floors for young two-person households;
— a day centre for up to 30 elderly people from the wider community.

The scheme originated with East Cambridgeshire District Council, who had identified the need for further elderly persons' accommodation in Ely and readily accepted that some form of specialised provision for frail elderly people was worthy of consideration. Even so, it was appreciated that providing and managing warden-controlled sheltered housing was one thing, but to provide care and meals in a specialised scheme for frail elderly people was quite another. At an early stage the Council decided that it wished to explore the possibility of proceeding in partnership with another agency. Discussions took place with the Cambridge Housing Society, who had a long and successful experience of providing and managing just such accommodation. At that time it became known that the Bedford House site would soon be available, following the reorganisation of secondary education in Ely, and the county council were approached about its purchase.

The next thing that happened illustrates the value of regular formal and informal contacts between officers of different authorities. In the course of discussions both at the county Chief Housing Officers' Group and in the joint consultative committee, the Director of Social Services came to know of the proposals. It was suggested that the site was large enough to allow space for the county council to provide a day centre and specialist unit for the elderly mentally infirm – the need for these services in Ely having already been accepted in principle – and so the seeds of an ambitious cooperative venture were sown. With approval of the various authorities concerned they started to germinate.

The basic structure of the package was to be as follows:

1   The East Cambridgeshire District Council to fund the purchase of the site and the cost of the housing development for the Cambridge Housing Society.
2   The Housing Society to build and manage the two-person flats, elderly persons' flats and specialised sheltered housing, giving the Council 75% nomination rights.

3   The county council to provide and manage the day centre on the ground floor of the original Bedford House.
4   The county council to build and manage the EMI unit, which would be an integral part of the new building, and share kitchens and some other facilities with the specialised housing scheme.

Not everything ran smoothly. The County Council had difficulty in finding the capital for the EMI unit. The situation was saved by a most unusual decision by the Department of the Environment. Always interested in this scheme, they made the exceptional decision of classing the EMI unit as housing accommodation eligible for housing association grant. Despite the county council's financial difficulties, the scheme has now started. It is to be funded substantially by the District Council but with the help of a small payment of capital and a transfer of capital allocation from the county to the District Council. The county will continue to pay for the day centre.

The advantages of such a joint scheme are obvious; a range of provision for elderly people on one site; one architect, one client; the efficient use of staff and the sharing of facilities. Three agencies there may be, each with different statutory responsibilities but the service will be unified, sensibly coordinated and integrated.

Community care call

There are many examples of intercommunication systems linked to a central control up and down the country. In some areas, the authority providing the central control room facility may seek customers from other areas to help balance the budget. The Cambridge Community Care Call Scheme is technically similar but differs from most others in that it is a joint scheme managed by an independent group. The idea was conceived in the deliberations of the Cambridge Health Authority Joint Development Team (Elderly). The introduction of an area-wide intercommunication network was envisaged with the following features:

1   The central control room equipment was to be paid for by joint finance and a grant from social services.
2   Instead of setting up a control room from scratch, use would be made of an existing facility owned and run by a private company called the Cambridge Medical Answering Service; charges would be levied on the user.
3   All peripheral equipment in people's homes would be paid for by the user authorities. At first only the housing authorities made use of the system. It enabled them to extend emergency cover to their elderly tenants, both in and outside warden-controlled schemes, for 24 hours a day. By use of this scheme, people are

enabled to stay in their own homes or return to them earlier than might be the case otherwise. This is a further example of cooperation leading to an enhanced service to the recipient

Hereward House, Soham

The Bedford House scheme has served as a marker. Other such schemes may follow. One, under initial discussion at Hereward House, involves collaboration between the county and East Cambridgeshire District Council. In this case the county proposes to purchase additional land and dedicate it to enable the enlargement of an existing Category II sheltered housing scheme. As part of the proposed scheme the existing accommodation would be upgraded, making the whole suitable for frail elderly people. Occupied by more dependent people the scheme would meet the requirements of both housing and social services authorities. It would be a partnership. The social services department proposes to make a revenue contribution equivalent to the cost of providing increased levels of care. The DHSS has given a preliminary indication that the residents may be eligible to receive hostel allowance.

Housing and care: pointers for the future

Three examples have been given. They are but three of many across the country as a whole. They serve to illustrate what must be taken into account if an integrated housing and care service is to be offered to the public.

Joint working is not easy. It can only be achieved at a cost. Attitudes must change; new skills must be acquired, there must be patience and trust. Apart from these generalities one point has emerged from this experience of collaboration. It is that the joint planning and implementation of a scheme requires that the people representing the different agencies involved must be able to speak for their organisation and commit it on policy or budget matters. In the examples discussed above difficulties arose. The county council, because of its size, has a weakness. Unlike the district or housing associations, its elected members are removed from everyday events. Because of their structure and size, county councils seem to lack a single point of decision. One department's intentions may be frustrated or delayed by another. There is a weakness over accountability.

If the joint approach is to succeed and flourish in the future, as it must for the sake of the recipient of care, then there is much to be done. Those who have experience of making it work would emphasise that, above all, due attention must be given to attitude, training and accountability.

5 Negotiating resource transfers

Michael White

Lincolnshire County Council Social Services Department and South Lincolnshire Health Authority

The negotiations for resource transfers to Lincolnshire County Council from South Lincolnshire Health Authority which took place during 1985 and 1986 occurred against a background of preceding joint planning discussions during 1983 and 1984, which were to have a continuing influence on the course and outcome of subsequent events. A distinction is drawn between the two phases of negotiations because it was only during the latter phase that comprehensive joint planning arrangements were established at operational level, in an attempt to integrate each agency's total mental handicap care systems. Prior to that, joint planning was conducted largely at a centralised senior management level, and aimed to coordinate new service proposals within care in the community policies for people with a mental handicap inappropriately accommodated in hospitals. The significance of the distinction between the two phases of both negotiations and joint planning is that negotiations continued on a centralised basis during 1985 and 1986, separate to, although interacting with, the development of operational joint planning.

Phase one: central planning 1983–4

During 1983 and 1984 joint planning on mental handicap services consisted of collaboration by senior management of Lincolnshire County Council Social Services Department (SSD) with District Management Team members of the new South Lincolnshire (District) Health Authority (SLHA). This collaboration aimed at the development of SSD mental handicap services in South Lincolnshire in coordination with SLHA planning objectives agreed with Trent

Regional Health Authority (RHA) under central government's care in the community policy.

County council policy support for care in the community programme

Having welcomed the government's consultative document *Care in the Community*[1] in 1981, Lincolnshire County Council Social Services Committee[2] considered the resulting DHSS circular on *Care in the Community and Joint Finance*[3] at its meeting in June 1983.[4] The Committee concluded that a basis clearly existed to meet the main objective of transferring responsibility from the NHS to SSDs for patients no longer requiring hospital care.

Health authority resource priority for mental handicap services

SLHA initiated proposals to implement the circular in collaboration with Lincolnshire SSD later that same year. These stemmed from SLHA's priority aim to develop a new pattern of community-based services for people with a mental handicap. Its existing services were largely centred on obsolete institutional provision at Fleet Hospital, Holbeach (145 beds) and at St Peter's Hospital, Bourne (105 beds). Fleet Hospital was intended for closure in 1988/9 under long term strategic plans to be submitted to Trent RHA, for the period 1983/4 to 1993/4.[5]

SLHA plans for mental handicap provision during this period consisted of residential accommodation, day care and community mental handicap teams to be developed as a District priority in order to expedite the closure of Fleet as soon as community-based alternatives were in place. SLHA policy was to develop its future pattern of services for people with a mental handicap whose level of functioning involved severe mental and physical handicaps and behaviours. Its perception of their needs consisted of long-term residential care with a staff-to-patient ratio of up to 1:1 in NHS community units. This definition of health authority responsibility for mental handicap was based on an assessment of a person's present and potential functioning corresponding to the National Development Team's (NDT's) 'group IV' categorisation, devised for planning purposes.[6] Groups I to III, ie people with a mental handicap with least severe to moderately severe levels of functioning, were perceived to be potentially the responsibility of social services and other providers of community care for their non-medical needs.

Capital-led plans for health authority residential provision

SLHA's existing residential provision, in addition to the two obsolete hospitals, included a newly opened purpose-built unit providing 48 beds (plus day care) at Norton Lea, Boston. This was intended to be the largest unit of a local pattern of community provision to serve the scattered population of South Lincolnshire. Three further 24-place new units were planned to be developed by 1987 in Grantham, Spalding and Bourne. To these 72 new places, around a further 80 places were required between 1985 and 1988 to provide community care for people in NDT categories I, II and III at present resident in SLHA provision. Successful development of this combined programme of additional provision would allow the closure of Fleet Hospital as a whole. Plans would then be developed at a later stage of the strategic plan period for reduction in the size of St Peter's Hospital.

Division of responsibility for day care

Early in 1984 Trent RHA published policy guidelines[7] for strategic planning which, although sufficiently generalised to confirm SLHA strategies for residential and day care provision for people in NDT group IV, did anticipate that local authorities would eventually become responsible for day care services for all groups of people with a mental handicap, on an integrated basis. Lincolnshire SSD at this stage did not feel ready to accept responsibility for development of all-day services for people in NDT group IV, despite the fact that there were already limited numbers of people with severe handicaps receiving 'special care' day services in existing Adult Training Centre (ATC) provision. A division of responsibility for developing day care services, mirroring that for residential services, was therefore established at this early stage of joint planning. This was planned to involve day care provision by SLHA for people in NDT category IV in purpose-built annexes to the two existing SSD day centres at Grantham and Spalding, together with a new jointly used day centre to be developed at Bourne, and existing NHS provision at Boston.

Application of National Development Team planning guidelines

Following an assessment by health authority clinical psychology staff of the long-stay population of SLHA mental handicap accommodation in late 1983, a group of 81 patients was identified for possible transfer to SSD care. This group comprised 24 people in NDT group I estimated to require group home accommodation staffed at a ratio of one staff to eight persons; 27 people in NDT group II estimated to require group home accommodation immediately or after preparation for group home in a hostel staffed at a ratio of one staff to six persons; 30 people in NDT group III estimated to require community care after intensive training, and with a level of supervision involving residential staffing at a ratio of one staff to four persons.

Subsequent discussions by senior officers of both agencies led to a 'block planning' response to these generalised assessments of patient functioning, which was reported to Social Services Committee in April 1984.[8] A residential and day care 'package' was approved for implementation over four years using transferred NHS care in the community or joint finance resources. This was backed by a small element of jointly financed social worker participation in Community Mental Handicap Teams.

This initial package comprised the following elements: the purchase or rent of six group homes for 24 patients in NDT group I; the building of a 24-place hostel (plus provision of three places in existing SSD hostels) for 27 NDT group II patients; the building of a 30-place hostel for NDT group III patients; the provision of 81 day care places in new extended or existing SSD ATCs.

Direct and indirect consequences for social services of care in the community transfer plans

During the remainder of 1984 this package was expanded in scope to cover improvements in existing SSD hostel and day care staffing levels, and was later altered in content by replacing planned new hostel provision with group home provision. The significance of the package expansion to include improved daytime and new night cover in all existing SSD hostels, and updating of instructor-to-trainee ratios from 1:15 to 1:10 in all existing ATCs, was threefold. First, it provided access for the care in the community transfer programme to all the existing, as well as the expanded, network of SSD residential and day care provision in South Lincolnshire's main communities. Second, it involved using the care in the community programme to generally improve SSD residential and day care services in South Lincolnshire, benefiting people with a mental handicap living in the community as well as those to be transferred from hospitals. Third, it provided for the possibility of movement within static SSD hostel populations to staffed group homes, to the extent that any of the existing hostel provision was required for some of the people to be transferred from hospitals.

Financial context of health authority plans

The financial arrangements underpinning the 1984 proposals involved revenue transfers to total £676,000 on completion of the transfer of 83 persons, that is on average around £8,000 per person per annum. Two-thirds of this was to fund direct provision for persons to be transferred, and one-third to fund upgrading of existing community provision. All capital expenditure (up to £2.1m) was to be met from either joint finance or SLHA capital allocation. During the transitional four year period of the programme, before offsetting savings could be maximised after the closure of Fleet Hospital, additional bridging finance was to be sought from Trent RHA. To put the £0.7m revenue transfer from SLHA to Lincolnshire SSD in context,[9] SLHA expenditure on mental handicap services was planned to grow by 49% (£1.4m) over the Trent RHA strategic plan period 1984–94, that is from £2.8m to £4.2m annual revenue expenditure. After the closure of Fleet Hospital and the financing of both its own community provision and the transfer package, SLHA would still be maintaining its second obsolete hospital, St Peter's at Bourne. The £4.2m projected expenditure required to do all this would exceed the Trent RHA guideline for mental handicap services by £0.8m, and might only possibly reduce when plans were developed for the reduction in size of St Peter's Hospital.

Formal agreement proposed to underpin transfer timetable

In proposing the 1984 transfer package, SLHA emphasised that the phasing in of the SSD share to this was crucial to the successful completion of its programme. Social Services Committee was therefore made aware that 'implementation of the joint plan implied the cooperation of the County Council and the Health Authority in the planned use of resources.'[10] To this end it was mutually agreed that a formal agreement in respect of revenue and capital transfers would be implemented by the two parties. In the three months following approval by Social Services Committee of the original transfer package in April 1984, SLHA and SSD officers exchanged views on their respective requirements for inclusion in the formal agreement.

Requirements of formal agreement

SLHA indicated that they expected the formal agreement to be drawn up by Trent RHA's solicitor, in liaison with Lincolnshire County Council's County Solicitor. In summary, SLHA's specifications for the formal agreement included:

1   Accordance with the letter and spirit of the *Care in the Community Joint Finance* circular HC(83)6.

2   Definition of patients to be transferred and NHS financed

resources to provide SSD facilities to meet their needs, using NDT classification of patient dependency. Application of agreement to specific number of patients in NDT groups I, II and III and to specific facilities for their use, and, as vacancies arose, to other people moving from hospital or otherwise requiring hospital accommodation, in those same categories. NHS continuing care of NDT group IV patients.

3   Capital payments for all additional facilities required for patients transferred to be met by SLHA.

4   Revenue costs (net of DHSS benefits) to SSD of residential and day care costs of patients transferred, plus costs of improving staffing in existing residential and day care SSD establishments within SLHA boundaries.

5   Annual audit to ensure agreed levels of facilities maintained.

6   Commitment to continuation of revenue transfer for a period of five years, thereafter annual review on a mutual basis. Annual review of entire programme from its commencement, until such time as central government transfer of resources to local authorities occurs.

7   Arbitration arrangements to be included in case of failure to agree on implementation.

8   Commencement of the agreement to depend on progress of implementation arrangements for transfer of NDT group I patients to SSD supported group homes.

Lincolnshire SSD's only requirements at this stage were a reservation of the right to place patients transferred from hospitals into existing facilities according to individual needs, anywhere in the county and, if required, before additional facilities were available.

Progress reviewed on central planning phase

Discussions in 1984 between senior managers of the two agencies concluded in a December meeting which reviewed progress on:

1   Drawing up a first draft of an agreement;

2   SLHA obtaining special financial assistance from Trent RHA for the proposed transfer programme;

3   The consequences for the package of a revised model of residential care proposed by Social Services, involving substituting group homes for hostel care according to individual need, and

4   The need to establish joint planning arrangements at operational level in order to implement the programme. The meeting agreed to complete the revised package of proposals, including detailed financial estimates, and report to the March 1985 SLHA

member meeting. In the meantime it was agreed to establish operational joint planning arrangements early in the New Year.

Phase Two: Operational Joint Planning 1985–6

Local joint planning team established as 'Partnership Group'

In a meeting between SLHA Mental Handicap Unit's Operational Management Group and SSD officers in January 1985 it was agreed to establish a health and social services joint planning group for mental handicap services in South Lincolnshire. Terms of reference were to be developed from those of the equivalent joint planning 'Partnership' Team already established in South Derbyshire, which had been visited by SSD and North Lincolnshire Health Authority members and officers in late 1984. A 'core' membership of the South Lincolnshire Partnership Group was agreed to include the SLHA Unit Administrator (later to become Unit General Manager), the SLHA Unit Director of Nursing, Head of Psychology, and Unit Accountant; and from the SSD to include an Assistant Director (responsible for planning and development), a senior operational manager plus a middle manager, and two principal officers responsible for planning and development roles respectively. Cooption of officers from, for example, District Council Housing Departments or County Council Education Department would occur as and when appropriate. Voluntary agency and client representation would be established after further discussion. Among the priority items agreed for early action within the joint planning framework was the need to devise a system for assessing individual hospital residents' skills and relationships and to use this to assess staffing levels.

Partnership Group terms of reference

The new Partnership Group's terms of reference were as follows:

> The Partnership Group is responsible for the planning, development and management of comprehensive services for adults and children with mental handicaps who live within that part of the Lincolnshire County Council area that falls within the boundaries of the South Lincolnshire Health Authority.
>
> In developing and promoting these services the group will organise activities within the resources available and in accordance with the policies and strategies agreed by the health authority and the local authority.[11]

Joint planning aims: integration

As a joint planning model this was an explicit attempt to progress collaboration from centralised coordination towards operational integration.[12] The extent to which this model succeeded or failed is reflected in general by the course of joint planning between the two authorities over the next two years, and in particular by the negotiations for a resource transfer agreement which are the subject of this chapter.

Scope and content of joint planning

During 1985 the new Partnership Group met in eight full meetings interspersed with a number of smaller sub-group meetings. A central part of a wide-ranging programme of joint planning activities included the formulation of joint plans and policies on all main aspects of service provision.[13] These included policy papers on: a joint statement of philosophy; a team approach to care; community mental handicap teams; day care; residential care; assessment, evaluation and monitoring. Among other policy and planning issue areas considered during this intensive period of collaborative activity, the following list gives an indication of the field of concern: individual programme plans; staff training, including joint training; personnel policy facilitating staff transfer; policy in relation to the private residential sector; setting up of a mental handicap register; and development of joint planning structures at a local level for implementation of agreed plans.

Assessment of individual needs

Of particular importance to the process of securing any eventual agreement on a programme for implementation was to be a detailed assessment exercise conducted by Social Services officers on the groups of hospital residents proposed for transfer to SSD care. The progress of the assessment exercise during 1985, and the con-sequent re-evaluation by Social Services in 1986 of the resources required, were to have a critical influence on the course of negotiations which ran parallel to the joint planning process during these two years.

Negotiating stances emerge

During the first half of 1985, whilst the Partnership Group was commencing an extensive programme of policy formulation and operational joint planning, the first indications of the two authorities' respective negotiating stances were emerging within the parallel transfer negotiations.

Health authority attitude to rising costs

As early as December 1984, when Social Services had first confirmed a shift in its model of residential care, replacing additional hostel provision with group home development as a preferred option, with access to existing hostel provision if required, SLHA expressed some concern in this change in proposed provision. This concern reflected anxiety that group home provision could cost more than the hostel provision, which had been used as part of the basis of estimating bridging finance requirements with Trent RHA in 1984.

The revised transfer package was subsequently recosted by SSD on a 1984/5 price base at a total of £738,000 revenue and up to £1.7m capital for direct and indirect residential and day care provision for 83 people, and submitted to SLHA in March 1985. From the reactions of SLHA to these proposals it became apparent that a £700,000 revenue maximum ceiling for the transfer package had been identified by officers negotiating the resource transfer as a negotiating limit. SSD financial officers responded to this expectation by modifying resource assumptions down to a new revenue total of £712,000 (ie an average of about £8,600 per person).

Social Services attitude to uncertainties in care cover

At this point the issue of resource limitation to £700,000 spilled over into the Partnership forum, at its March 1985 meeting. The 'excess' amount of £12,000 became identified with estimated requirements by SSD for an allowance for night cover if required for the 29 persons in NDT group 1, to be accommodated in group homes. These 29 persons comprised 19 people already living in SLHA group homes situated adjacent to or in the locality of mental handicap hospitals, plus a further 10 people to be transferred into group homes either directly from hospital or from existing SSD hostel places requested for hospital transfers. The Social Services' view was that night cover should be available as an option if required, with the withdrawal of hospital responsibility in the case of existing group homes and to facilitate establishment of new group homes. SLHA's view was that the persons already in group homes required minimum support at present, and therefore night care was unnecessary in the future. There remained conflicting views from the two parties over the actual amount of informal support actually being given by NHS staff to people needing support in group homes, and the matter was not agreed.

An attempt to reach a financial resolution of the conflict in Partnership views took the form of a proposal to include separate reference in the proposed formal agreement to a sum of £12,000, to be drawn on only if night cover was required for individual group homes by social services.

Conflicting negotiating objectives

This particular example of early conflict illustrates the first signs of an underlying theme for the ensuing negotiations on the transfer agreement. On the one hand, SLHA continued its determination to limit the financial transfer to a level of real resources predetermined at the earliest 'block planning' stage of negotiations. On the other hand, there was a growing reservation by Social Services of the right to review resource requirements according to individuals' assessed needs.

Specificity versus flexibility

A further level of specificity introduced into the transfer negotiations at this stage early in 1985 concerned SLHA's request for details of costs and timescales for all transfers, to be incorporated in a second draft of the contractual document being prepared by the Trent RHA solicitor.

By July 1985 negotiations on financial procedures to be incorporated in the agreement had progressed to the stage at which SLHA forwarded a copy of the draft document to the County Council's solicitor. This provided Social Services with the first opportunity to comment in detail on the content of the contractual document which had been in the process of being drawn up for SLHA during the previous year. In its response to this draft, the most important requirement from Social Services' point of view concerned the need to specify a right for both parties to agree the classification of individual patients prior to transfer from hospital by a process of joint assessment. The rest of Social Services' response concerned general suggestions to edit and simplify the legalistic content of the draft contract, and attempts to insert some degree of flexibility into the contract's detailed specification.

It was anticipated that the setting up of 16 new group homes, including negotiations with several outside bodies, would in particular render a blueprint three-year timetable approach to implementation unrealistic.

Interaction of joint planning with transfer negotiations

SLHA's response to these comments in October 1985 revealed the beginning of a rift in collaborative relations, originating from both the Partnership joint planning forum and the separate negotiation process.

1   *Policy preconditions.* In the Partnership Group a dispute arose when it became apparent that SLHA regarded formal ratification by Social Services Committee of detailed joint policy statements as a precondition of the signing of a resource transfer contract. Given the changes in policy, attitudes and expectations entailed, for example, in evolution from existing traditional ATC practice to a Social Education Centre preferred model of day care, Social Services officers reserved the right to pursue the approval process for policy development independently of resource transfers. The use of policy changes preconditions by SLHA was regarded by Social Services as displaying not only an unacceptable use of resource transfers by one agency to encroach on the other agency's independence, but also evidence of a lack of trust in their sincerity or ability to implement mutually agreed directions for policy development.

2   *Joint assessment.* In the transfer negotiations, SLHA's reaction to Social Services requirement in the contract for mutually agreed joint assessment to precede actual patient transfers, expressed itself as an insistence that the original NDT groupings and numbers would remain the basis of resource requirements to meet total needs, which would be fixed at a maximum revenue of £700,000, plus a discretionary £12,000 sum. From the Health Authority's point of view, therefore, previously defined estimates of facilities to provide Social Services care for 83 persons, grouped by NDT planning categories, and costed to a maximum revenue transfer sum, remained the central facet of the revenue transfer agreement.

3   *Joint monitoring.* The disagreement on the status of joint policies in the transfer negotiations escalated within the partnership joint planning meeting in November 1985, when it became clear that evaluation and monitoring policies and procedures were also regarded by SLHA as prerequisites to revenue transfer. SLHA officers regarded such procedures as a means of verifying that resources transferred were buying an acceptable quality of service for former patients. Social Services officers, while agreeing in principle to qualitive evaluation and monitoring (in addition to normal financial monitoring), again objected to the implied lack of trust of one agency by another in making such specific proposals a precondition of the transfer agreement. These proposals involved a joint monitoring team of

health and social services officers, which would have scrutinised practice in both agencies. Social Services officers again expressed concern that the policy strings attached to resource transfers in the form of these particular evaluation and monitoring procedures posed an unacceptable intrusion on one agency's management and accountability by another, especially because the intention of ostensibly mutual procedures was so explicitly linked to a one-sided financial relationship.

Management attempts to resolve differences

Towards the end of 1985 it was becoming increasingly clear to senior management on both sides that a meeting including Chief Officers was required in order to clear the way for any agreement on negotiations. This would provide an opportunity for an exchange of views on outstanding issues, including the status of joint policies and joint assessment, but also focusing on more fundamental differences of view, from which these issues in part arose. These were, in essence, the insistence by SLHA on the County Council meeting legally binding contractual obligations within a fixed resource limit. On its part, Social Services (supported by the County Council's treasurer) wanted review requirements built into the agreement, related to individuals' assessed resource needs over time and also taking into account unforeseen changes in external circumstances affecting implementation, outside the local authority's control. Even more profoundly, there was mounting concern on the Social Services side over the feasibility of a legal agreement as the basis of resource transfer. With its comprehensive attempt to specify resource costings and phasings, it appeared to be increasingly illsuited to the realities of implementing a care in the community programme.

After two inconclusive meetings in December 1985 and February 1986 during which all these issues and concerns were fully explored and expressed by senior managers of both agencies, the County Council's requirements were still not met in the resulting redrafts of the legal agreement produced for SLHA by Trent Regional Solicitor.

'Head of Agreement' initiative to break impasse

By March 1986 it was therefore clear to Social Services that an initiative not based on the cumbersome framework of the legal agreement was necessary in order to break the impasse. Because SLHA was not willing to conduct the transfer under the normal memorandum of agreement arrangements used for joint finance schemes and care in the community programmes elsewhere, Social Services offered a compromise arrangement in the interest of progress, consisting of a much shorter and less formal 'Heads of Agreement'. This was initially drafted by the County Council's solicitor and Social Services staff and eventually, after development jointly with North Lincolnshire Health Authority as well as with SLHA, comprised the following elements:

1 *Nature of the agreement*: a description of the nature of the agreement, covering a mutually agreed assessment of needs met by the transfer of resources contained in an updatable schedule, subject to continuing review and amendment by the joint planning Partnership Group. Policies underlying the implementation of the agreement were to be those of the health authority and the County Council, with the Partnership Group responsible for the coordination of the implementation of such policies, for the monitoring of standards of care, and for making recommendations to each parent authority, via the joint consultative committee.

2 *Financial arrangements*: covering the transfer of revenue and capital resources to enable the transfer of patients, the amounts to be detailed in reviewable schedules on a scheme by scheme basis. This included arrangements for payment; financial monitoring and audit; a financial review within the overall allocation of funds for mental handicap services within the budget constraints of the Health Authority and County Council, and the continuation of transfer of funds until permanent arrangements are made by central government.

3 *Review*: monitoring the annual review of operational and financial collaborative arrangements for the care in the community programme via the joint consultative committee.

4 *Management of the schemes*: including arrangements for access to all existing as well as additional Social Services facilities by the patients transferred, having regard to local ties where they existed. This was a description of the respective roles of the Partnership Group in relation to joint consultative committee and its advisory 'joint policy officer group' drawn from senior management teams of each agency in Lincolnshire (equivalent in most authorities to the joint care planning team). There were also undertakings to maintain existing resource levels to mental handicap services by both authorities; and of the right to reconsider commitments to agreed strategies in the event of unilateral action substantially reducing resources.

Focus of negotiations switches from South to North Lincolnshire

After the initial rejection by SLHA in April 1986 of Social Services' proposal to substitute a Heads of Agreement approach for the Regional Health Authority's formal contract, the focus for both operational joint planning and the initiative for negotiating resource transfer switched from the County Council's point of view from South to North Lincolnshire.

Lincolnshire County Council Social Services Department and North Lincolnshire Health Authority

Joint planning collaborative arrangements on a care in the community programme for transfers of people with a mental handicap had been established between Lincolnshire County Council SSD and North Lincolnshire Health Authority (NLHA) a little later in 1985 than those with SLHA, and benefited from this for a number of reasons.

Timetable

First, the timescale for the closure of NLHA's main mental handicap hospital at Harmston Hall near Lincoln was longer than that for Fleet Hospital in South Lincolnshire. Under Trent RHA plans it was originally expected to close by 1992/3, compared to the closure date of 1988 for Fleet, later extended to 1989.

Learning from local experience

Second, lessons for both joint planning and transfer negotiations could be learned by following a few steps behind the progress of arrangements between Social Services and the neighbouring SLHA, for both their positive and negative aspects.

The joint planning model developed between Social Services and SLHA (itself adapted from one used in Derbyshire) had been simply adopted for use in North Lincolnshire, and a Partnership Group established in April 1985. Similarly, the considerable collaborative work put in by SLHA and Social Services officers in producing comprehensive joint statements of policy during 1985 could simply be adopted wholesale by the Partnership Group for North Lincolnshire. This was deliberately supported by Social Services officers within the NLHA Partnership Group, as a means of establishing countywide policies with both district health authorities.

The financial basis and resource components of the care in the community programme for mental handicap services in North Lincolnshire shared some important characteristics, but also some differences – in particular in the models of care, the division of responsibilities, and the relationships of agency functions.

Financial context of Health Authority plans

NLHA expenditure on mental handicap services at the beginning of the Trent RHA strategic planning period 1984–94 was already double the regional guideline level, being based on the provision of two obsolete mental handicap hospitals at Harmston Hall and Caistor, totalling 528 beds, with a historic role covering parts of South Lincolnshire and South Humberside, as well as North Lincolnshire. Under RHA agreed 10 year strategy, it was due to reduce this resource base to 50% above regional guideline level (ie from £4.8m to £4.2m annual revenue expenditure).[14] Over the strategic planning period this will involve the closure of Harmston Hall, the transfer of Caistor Hospital to Grimsby Health Authority, and the development of a community-based mental handicap service provided by health and social services, together with the private and voluntary sectors.

Regional Health Authority financial strategy for care in the community

Like SLHA, NLHA can draw on Trent RHA bridging money to facilitate this. In 1984 SLHA had agreed special assistance from the RHA to expedite its ambitious plans to replace Fleet Hospital by a community-based service in four years. By 1985 Trent RHA had drawn up an explicit financial strategy[15] to assist all its constituent district health authorities in their care in the community plans for mental handicap and mental health services. As well as specifying that it expected at least two-thirds of joint finance allocations to be spent on care in the community programmes for these two client groups, the financial strategy established a regional development reserve fund to loan bridging money to districts for 18 months, in order to ease the burden of providing community-based services for patients transferred from hospital, whilst maintaining reducing hospital services. The bridging fund contributed up to £12,500 per patient transferred into health service community-based accommodation, and around £6,000 per patient transferred into Social Services or other non-health service community provision. It is worth noting that these were arbitrary levels based on the average costs of existing hospital-based services in the case of the higher figure, and were not regarded as norms for the total financing of community-based services.

In both SLHA and NLHA planned transfer programmes to social services the £6,000 per head figure was considerably exceeded. As an added incentive to districts using the bridging money, Trent required the payback of only 60% of money lent, thus allowing the retention of 40%. NLHA planned to use this assistance, as well as using its own development resources, to implement its mental handicap strategy.

Joint planning aims: coordination

From the outset of joint planning between NLHA Mental Handicap Unit and Social Services, the model of collaboration adopted was envisaged to maintain separate service accountability arrangements for the two agencies, but with coordinated local development and later management of provision. The terms of reference for the North Lincolnshire Partnership Group reflected this in a subtle difference in wording from that of the equivalent document in South Lincolnshire. For South Lincolnshire the original aim for the Partnership had been 'planning development and management of comprehensive service', ie a supposedly integrative model of collaboration. The limits of this approach were soon tested in joint planning disagreements in the South Lincolnshire Partnership, stemming from Social Services' resistance of resource transfer conditions being used by SLHA to determine local authority policy and practice. In North Lincolnshire the equivalent aim for the Partnership was 'planning, development and coordination of management of comprehensive services'[16], ie a step back from attempting integration to a coordinative model of collaboration.[17]

Local basis of service development

As in South Lincolnshire, Community Mental Handicap Team boundaries were designated to be as far as possible coterminous with Social Services operational districts (or their sub-divisions), which in turn are coterminous with district council boundaries. The NLHA Unit General Manager, however, announced at an early stage plans for locality-based managers for the new community mental handicap services, both to manage health services directly, and to coordinate service delivery with that provided locally by Social Services and by the private and voluntary sector. This organisational arrangement was explicitly designed to offer a comprehensive service, coordinated to avoid duplication, in order that clients would not fall between agency divisions.

Joint planning programme 1985-6

During a one-year joint planning period spanning April 1985 to March 1986, and involving eight formal Partnership Group meetings and a greater number of informal working sub-group meetings, a care in the community, programme comparable with that being developed with SLHA was agreed between NLHA and Social Services, together with regional and local representatives of Mencap, and the North Lincolnshire Community Health Council.

The original programme agreed in March 1986 involved transfer of 76 patients in NDT groups I–III to Social Services.[18] Revenue resources totalling £717,000 (averaging £9,400 per person) and up to £1.45m capital were to be deployed to provide access for persons transferred from hospital to a pattern of additional and improved existing residential and day care services in the main local population centres of North Lincolnshire. Residential provision was to be based on group homes, with access to hostels if required. Day care was to be based on a Social Education model of care, using NHS resource transfers to improve overall staffing ratios within all existing, as well as additional, day centre provision.

Models of care and division of agency responsibilities

The differences in the models of care and division of agency responsibilities, compared with the SLHA programme, centred on health service residential provision for 160 people in NDT group IV, and day care for people in all functional dependency groups. In line with national thinking on normalisation principles, NLHA intended to base all its residential provision on staffed group homes. Similarly, and in line with Trent RHA guidelines, NLHA from the beginning of joint planning discussions in 1985 made it clear that it expected to negotiate a further revenue resource package to enable Social Services to provide unified day care services to people with all mental handicap dependency characteristics.[19] The seven-year implementation timescale for the NLHA programme (compared to the three to four years for the SLHA programme), combined with changes in Social Services senior management, enabled this proposal to be accepted as a basis for negotiation.

Basis of negotiating transfer agreement

At the beginning of the joint planning programme in 1985, the basis for negotiating resource transfers to finance the North Lincolnshire package was expected on both sides to follow the same legal contractual pattern being pursued in South Lincolnshire.

By March/April 1986, however, when the North Lincolnshire programme was formally agreed as policy by NLHA and Social Services Committee, the lessons of the continuing failure to agree the SLHA contract could be learned. The Heads of Agreement initiative by the County Council in March 1986 (produced in an attempt to break the negotiating deadlock with SLHA) coincided with agreement in North Lincolnshire on a care in the community transfer programme, and was taken up positively by NLHA as the basis of resource transfer. NLHA's main requirements for incorporation within the agreement were: flexibility of implementation (hence the use of schedules for individual schemes to be attached as agreed over time); and periodic review within the joint planning framework of the Partnership Group (hence the specification of the Partnership Group's relationship with each agency's separate accountability structure), as well as collaborative machinery such as the joint policy officer group and joint consultative committee.

Interaction of style and content of joint planning

The flexibility requirement in the Heads of Agreement was a reflection of the style of joint planning within the NLHA Partnership Group. In contrast to the centralised conduct of contractual negotiations parallel with and interacting with SLHA Partnership Group joint planning, NLHA joint planning and Heads of Agreement negotiations were largely delegated to Unit General Manager level, with central planning and Treasurer's backup as required. This discretion at Unit level allowed a pragmatic and flexible response to major changes in circumstances during the course of NLHA Partnership's joint planning during 1986, without disrupting progress.

These changes were the rapid growth of the private residential sector in North Lincolnshire, and the implications of the continuing joint assessment programme for individuals' actual, as opposed to theoretical, care needs in proposed group homes.

Impact of private sector on joint planning

The use of private residential accommodation for some of the people to be transferred from hospital provided the Partnership Group with an opportunity to accelerate the care in the community programme as long as private sector provision met the agreed model of care. Following discussions within the Partnership Group involving a representative of the private sector, a modified version of the residential care model was agreed, to encompass residential provision by the private and voluntary sector as well as by health and social services.

Impact of reassessment of individual needs

The use of private sector placements, in particular for patients in NDT groups I and II, released resources within the transfer package which were retained rather than saved, to meet higher staffing requirements in Social Services group homes. These requirements were based on individual assessments of those people in NDT groups II and III still in hospital, and were considerably higher than originally estimated. NLHA nursing and psychology staff confirmed the social work assessments of these people's actual care needs. Consequently, the Social Services group home component of the package was reduced from 76 to 37 persons, but at approximately double the staffing resources previously agreed. Day care requirements were similarly reduced from 76 to 47 places to reflect the reality of individuals' assessed needs, and included 10 places for people transferred to private residential care.

Revised social services transfer package

The net result of those changes, some aspects of which are still subject to further joint planning discussions at the time of writing in June 1987, is a transfer package containing all the original resource elements, but focused on smaller numbers. Planned revenue transfers for 37 residential and 47 day care places total £532,000 (averaging £13,000 annual costs for a person receiving County Council residential and day care), whilst anticipated capital transfers have halved from up to £1.45m to up to £0.63m, due to use of the private sector. This programme is due to be implemented over three years.

The Heads of Agreement negotiations were pursued over six months to a successful conclusion between NLHA and Lincolnshire County Council, being signed at Chief Officer level in October 1986 and ratified in a member signing ceremony in January 1987.[20]

Postscript on South Lincolnshire Health Authority and Lincolnshire County Council Social Services Department negotiations

During the same period of 1986, SLHA and Social Services failed to conclude an identical Heads of Agreement, despite attempts involving senior management of both agencies and, latterly, members of both authorities. The total cost limit approach adopted by SLHA from the start of negotiations had in particular proved too inflexible to withstand the County Council's continuing insistence during 1986 on a review of resource requirements related to assessed needs. The failure to agree a legal contract, against SLHA expectations, and the consequent damage to relationships at different levels during the lengthy joint planning and negotiating process, led eventually to the rejection by SLHA of the Heads of Agreement at a joint officer-member meeting in October 1986.

What was agreed at that meeting was an undertaking to proceed transfers with a tripartite programme between SLHA, Social Services and Mencap's Homes Foundation, without any formal agreement between the two statutory authorities, but on an incremental basis. As a consequence of the delays in the negotiating process, at the same meeting a decision was made to extend the target closure date for Fleet Hospital by a year to March 1989.

The emergence of a voluntary sector agency as a major partner in providing residential group homes promises to be the South Lincolnshire equivalent of inclusion of the private sector in the North Lincolnshire programme. In both cases access to central government finance, via DHSS supplementary benefit for private and voluntary residential care, is providing additional resources to the two Lincolnshire transfer packages, enabling Social Services and NHS provision to be financed within each health authority's care in the community budget limits.

During the first half of 1987 both South Lincolnshire Health Authority and the County Council Social Services Committee approved policy reports underpinning the revised multiagency package, subject to health authority overall financial limits for the total care in the community programme being met.[21]

With the benefit of hindsight it must be said that such an incremental basis for a resource transfer programme, including as it did standard DHSS audit requirements and procedures between respective treasurers already available under existing arrangements for care in the community and joint finance, could have been proceeded with up to two years earlier. As one Social Services latecomer to the negotiations sceptically commented on the previous attempts to draw up a legal contract: 'If I had wanted to get an agreement I would not have started from here'.

Lessons learned and signposts

What are the precedents for success rather than failure in the resource transfer negotiating process that can be identified from the differing courses of events described for South Lincolnshire and North Lincolnshire? The following broad principles are suggested for consideration:

A balance between financial resource-led planning and needs assessment-led planning is required. Financial limits on programmes are clearly a fact of life in service planning, but attempts to force care in the community packages into too rigid a financial straitjacket at the outset of negotiations are doomed to generate interagency dispute and programme delay or breakdown. Joint planners should therefore avoid beginning with the kind of detailed block planning approach favoured by treasurers, whether it is revenue- or capital resource-led. Instead, a needs-led approach is preferable as a starting point, involving a process of joint assessment of client requirements extending over both the joint planning and implementation phases of a programme. Such an iterative process, providing as it does a flexible response to the uncertainties inherent in large-scale service developments, can then be operated alongside, or even within, the setting of cost limits eventually agreed for a package or programme.

The establishment of joint planning arrangements should precede, not follow, financial negotiations. Resource negotiations should be delegated as far as possible to the same level of management as joint planning. The process of agreeing joint models of care involved in establishing comprehensive joint planning arrangements on the 'Partnership' model described, despite its potential for conflict between different agencies and interest groups represented, also provides a forum for learning across agency boundaries, and the preconditions for mutual understanding, respect and trust in resource negotiations.

Those resource negotiations, however, need to be integrated and delegated as far as possible to the same management level as joint planning if the investment in joint planning machinery is to pay dividends in the form of respective managers' personal commitment to positive relationships across agency boundaries.

The imbalance in power between agencies controlling NHS finance and agencies collaborating in providing community care is more apparent than real. District health authorities committed to achieving the setting up of community care services and hospital closures, within regional health authority and central government targets, cannot control the negotiating process with local authorities and other agencies simply on the basis of control of existing NHS financial resources. In order to achieve their care in the community goals, DHAs are obliged to collaborate with local authorities, voluntary agencies and the private sector on the basis of mutual respect and mutual self-interest, rather than simply as client and contractor. Thus, for example, the voluntary and private sector's access to DHSS benefits for residential care and SSDs' existing community-based provision, particularly in day care, provides these agencies with significant bargaining strength in negotiations.

Resource transfer agreements should incorporate sufficient flexibility to allow review in response to changes in client need or the financial environment. The flexibility underpinned by policy commitment afforded by the less formal Heads of Agreement approach allows a permanent review in response to changes in client need or the financial environment. More formal contractual agreement requires a level of certainty in defining resource requirements in relation to assessed need, which is not available early in the joint planning process, but may be appropriate for well-defined components of a comprehensive community care package.

Parallel negotiations produce a positive learning effect. When a local authority or other agency is negotiating simultaneously with more than one district health authority, progress with one can be used to influence progress with another, thus introducing a mutual learning element into otherwise localised joint planning.

A mutual respect for each agency's motives, standards and independence is both a prerequisite and an outcome of collaboration. Without being platitudinous, this is easier to express than to achieve, but cannot be omitted from consideration. Interagency monitoring and evaluation of care in the community programme implementation poses considerable challenges if it is to be attempted, and is doubly complicated when agencies such as SSDs occupy two roles, both as service providing partners in joint planning and as statutory registration and inspection authorities for the private and voluntary sector.

To conclude on a cautionary note, the financial consequences of assessment-led, as opposed to finance-led, planning are clearly inflationary. The progressive increase of average costs per person during the negotiation of both SLHA and NLHA packages, following reassessments of hospital patients to be transferred, clearly demonstrates the current maxim that community care is not cheaper than institutional care.

Notes

1 DHSS (1981), *Health Service Department – Care in the Community – A consultative document on Moving Resources for Care in England*, HC(81)9/LAC(81)5.
2 Lincolnshire County Council Social Services Committee, 15 October 1981 (Paper E).
3 DHSS (1983), *Care in the Community and Joint Finance*, HC/83/6/LAC(83)5.
4 Lincolnshire County Council Social Services Committee, 16 June 1983 (Paper E).
5 Trent Regional Health Authority (1986), *Better Health for Trent – A Plan for Action 1983/4–1993/4*, p 244.

6   DHSS (1978), *Helping Mentally Handicapped People in Hospital: A Report to the Secretary of State for Social Services by the National Development Group*, p 99.

7   Trent Regional Health Authority (1984), *Regional Policy Guidelines for Strategic Planning of Services for the Mentally Handicapped.*

8   Lincolnshire County Council Social Services Committee, 12 April 1984 (Paper E).

9   Trent Regional Health Authority (1986), *op cit*, pp 110–12.

10 Lincolnshire County Council (1984), *op cit.*

11 Lincolnshire County Council/North Lincolnshire Health Authority/ South Lincolnshire Health Authority (1986), *Statement of Joint Policies*, Appendix 7(b).

12 Davidson, S M 'Planning and Coordination of Social Services in Multi Agency Contexts' in *Social Services Review*, vol 50, no. 1.

13 Lincolnshire County Council/North Lincolnshire Health Authority/ South Lincolnshire Health Authority (1986), *op cit.*

14 Trent Regional Health Authority (1986), *op cit*, pp 110–12.

15 Trent Regional Health Authority (1985), *Caring for the Mentally Handicapped and Mentally Ill in Trent Region – Financial Strategy.*

16 Lincolnshire County Council/North Lincolnshire Health Authority/ South Lincolnshire Health Authority (1986), *op cit*, Appendix 7(a).

17 Davidson, *op cit.*

18 Lincolnshire County Council Social Services, 10 April 1986 (Paper D).

19 Lincolnshire County Council Social Services Committee, 9 April 1987 (Paper F).

20 Lincolnshire County Council/North Lincolnshire Health Authority (1987), *Heads of Agreement Relating to Mentally Handicapped Patients.*

21 Lincolnshire County Council Social Services Committee, 4 June 1987 (Paper C).

6 Joint planning in the face of uncertainty

Greg Parston and Dick Stockford

This chapter describes an experiment in joint planning. The experiment – undertaken during a two-day conference in East Anglia – was intended to simulate how planners from different organisations, with different responsibilities, objectives and perceptions, could work together to plan an agreed and integrated joint pattern of services in the face of uncertainty. The findings are crude and preliminary, but they do point to new ways of developing agreed agenda for joint provision of local services.

Dealing with uncertainty and unknowability

Planning is plagued with uncertainty. It has been shown time and again that it is impossible to predict with any certainty the future environment within which organisations will find themselves working. As a result, attempts to plan now the actions and developments that will be required over the longer-term – that is, to design the masterplan for the future thought probable now – are likely to have little to do with the future conditions which actually do occur.

The uncertainties surrounding the development of health and social services are numerous; many of them are outside the control or even the direct influence of health authorities and local authorities. Yet they significantly affect the pattern of services for which those authorities are responsible. They include changes in demographic patterns, for example, growth or movement of local populations, or shifts in the patterns of illness and disabilities; changes in government policy, such as new priorities given to different types of need or to different categories of patients and clients; changes in the economic environment, for instance, the introduction of national restrictions on local authority expenditure or temporary shifts in health services' budget allocations; changes in technology, for example, new developments in communication or in diagnostic equipment; and changes in health and social services themselves, which could include innovations in treatment procedures or a shifting emphasis to preventive measures. The direction in which these types of changes will occur and their impacts on the patterns of services that will be required are impossible to predict; some of them – as the recent presentation of AIDS shows – are unknowable in advance.

In the planning of joint care patterns, external uncertainties and unknowabilities are exacerbated by the separate and sometimes conflicting values and goals within the organisations involved. Differences in values and goals need not be rooted in political ideology, and indeed may have much more to do with the uncontrollable environmental influences on the separate organisations. For example, what a local authority may wish to achieve in terms of, say, fulfilling an electoral mandate for decentralised services, may run contrary to the ambitions of its health authority partner to retain more centralised, but economic, services in order to meet imposed financial restrictions. Moreover, the composition and values of each authority are subject – directly or not – to electoral whim; even the actions by one authority today may be regarded as inappropriate by the same, reconstituted authority come the next election.

The difficulty of coming to an agreed agenda

In the face of these difficulties, the history of joint planning between local authorities and health authorities can be parodied as an elaborate court ritual, where the ritual itself frequently has been more important than the issues it is meant to address, and where the opportunities for avoiding issues are legion. There is, however, a growing realisation that joint planning means more than just joint meetings. It demands, in short, an agreement about joint planning agenda and a mutual recognition of the difficult task of managing uncertain conditions. But even agreement does not ease the problem. For joint planning to succeed, planners must address directly the seemingly insuperable barriers to cooperation and coordination which belie the simplicity of many of the imperatives associated with the need to provide care in the community.

These barriers, different in their effect and time, are reducible to three. None are unique to care in the community and none are unique to the public sector, but all represent significant hurdles to the ardent planners who are seeking to design a humane, effective and responsive service.

First is the thorny problem of the different organisational context: the environment, both economic and political, in which all planners must operate and over which they exercise little or no control. Here it is different perceptions of perhaps similar conditions and, more dramatically, different expectations of future conditions that hinders the joint development of policies. The health planner from a 'non-political' – or at least non-electoral – health authority is likely to view the world quite differently from the local authority planner who is aware that a new council will be elected before the planning stage is complete, and that a changed political balance could mean a different approach to joint planning altogether. Equally, the health authority planner may well envy the local authority planner's relative freedom to move resources around within a budget base, whilst the local authority planner would envy the size and certainty of health authority revenue. These differences in perception are powerful in determining action. Individual planners' views of the future state of their organisations' economies, for example, are bound to influence how they shape and develop their own plans, as well as their expectations about outcome. Yet, whilst planners can speculate on these differences, their speculation is not likely to alter the eventual shape of the political or economic contexts in which they work. Unless some way can be found to accommodate these differences in perception, expectation and reality, the ability of planners to work jointly is limited.

A second and more powerful barrier is that the organisations for whom joint planners plan have different and, in some cases, contradictory objectives. In many cases, of course, objectives will not be clearly stated and so a precursor to joint planning must be their explication, something which can be conceptually difficult and politically uneasy for the authorities involved. In the case of care in the community, it is apparent that whilst the objective of joint or shared care represents an important formal objective of both health and local authorities, this objective sometimes exists only to the extent of ensuring that the partner organisation is made responsible for meeting it! That organisations with palpably obvious responsibilities for meeting human need can arrive at this position may be disturbing, but it is at least understandable. Taking the example of health and social services further, their differences have been well summarised in the Nodder Report and tabulated in Table 6.1.

In view of these differences it is not surprising that partner organisations have difficulty in agreeing any similar objectives at all, a problem increasingly cited in the call for unitary authorities. Some means of harmonising different, and sometimes competing, objectives must be found before any effective joint planning can be undertaken.

The third barrier, obvious from the summary in Table 6.1, is that the organisations may well have considerably different responsibilities and, in terms of their accountabilities, very different publics.

TABLE 6.1 Care in the community – the structure and organisation of health and social services (adopted from the Nodder Report)

Item	Health service	Social services
Accountability	To DHSS	Largely controlled locally
Membership	Appointed	Elected
Finance	From Exchequer	Nearly two-thirds raised locally
Control/public accountability	Health authorities and CHCs are separate	Elected members perform both roles
Geographical boundaries	Hospital catchments	An amalgamation of traditional communities
Internal structures	RHAs and AHAs are corporate	SSDs are part of the local authorities with wider functions
	Confined to health interests	Other duties, for example juvenile delinquency
Dominating skills	Medical/nursing	Social work
	Long history of training	Many staff untrained
Responsibility	Individual clinical responsibility	Most responsibilities are to the local authority leading to more member involvement
	Dispersed	Managerial control more specific

Source: DHSS, *Organisational and Management Problems of Mental Illness Hospitals. Report of a Working Group,* 1981.

Even where responsibilities overlap, the pressure to clarify each organisation's accountability (because, if nothing else, 'the best use of public money must be made') is considerable and often not in the best interests of joint planning (nor, incidentally, the best use of public money overall).

A way forward

If joint planning is to assist health and local authorities to overcome these barriers, to respond appropriately to uncertain future changes, and in the end to provide a humane and effective service, it cannot attempt to master the environment or the future. It cannot pretend that barriers do not exist; nor can predictions of the environmental changes or the emergence of different values that will largely determine the agencies' future actions be made. A way forward for joint planning is to use the tools of planning to explore and manage differences and uncertainties, rather than to try to eliminate them.

Whilst planning cannot make absolute predictions about the consequences of any planning decisions taken today, the tools and procedures of planning can be adapted to help construct alternative pictures of the future environment, alternatives which are not impossible and which pose meaningfully different consequences for current actions. These multiple futures would enable services managers and providers to explore the possible range of consequences of decisions taken today, to examine what would or could happen if a certain type of future materialises. It would be possible to investigate different long-term developments of services which might prove advantageous should particular patterns of events come to pass. It also would be possible to pose questions such as 'How does this action help meet our different organisations' objectives if a particular set of future conditions occurs?' and 'Do other actions retain more flexibility by affording a viable solution across a broader range of future conditions?'

In this fashion, authorities which are engaged in planning for joint provision of services could develop shortlists of 'robust' joint planning actions – that is, actions which improve the current performance of both organisations and which would be mutually recognised as contributing to anticipated satisfactory performance under a range of possible future environments. Such shortlists could provide a basis for informed discussion and negotiation between authorities – even those with very different objectives – about immediate agreed agenda for action.

This type of multi-future planning is not uncommon in organisations which face high levels of uncertainty and unknowability. In the

National Health Services, for example, there have been and are several experiments with multi-future planning. A similar planning approach, developed by the Ottawa-Carleton Regional District Health Authority in Canada (see Best, Parston and Rosenhead 1986), employed a multi-future methodology which was thought by the current authors to provide a particularly useful way of trying to deal with the uncertainties and barriers of joint planning. The methodology entailed the use of a modified Delphi technique in order to help people, with very different perceptions of the future, identify the possible alternative contexts within which health and social services might be provided. These alternative futures were used to ask the sort of 'what if' questions posed above and then to identify robust short-term actions. It was this technique which the authors used to experiment – in a very crude and preliminary fashion – with a new way of planning joint care patterns among health authority and local authority planners in East Anglia.

The way the opportunity arose in East Anglia and the context of the workshop

Potted history of joint planning in the area

The East Anglian Regional Health Authority covers three county councils, ten district councils and eight district health authorities. Although the joint planning circulars increasingly exhort, through the medium of the joint consultative committee process, local authority and health authority interaction, this tends to be on a sub-regional basis in East Anglia. Some RHAs, like North West Thames and Trent, have been particularly assertive in their joint planning roles, particularly in relation to services for mentally handicapped people. The reasons for this are beyond the scope of this chapter, but the East Anglian Regional Health Authority could not be said to have a high profile in this respect.

Thus, unless mediated by the Region, there is unlikely to be much contact between individual interacting parts. The accident of the 'overlap areas' in district health authorities, along with the coincidental movement of staff between organisations, changes this. 'Overlap areas' straddle more than one personal social services authority and thus by definition more than one housing authority. As a result, such areas have the opportunity (or the headache) of straddling not only different local authority policies but also different planning frameworks. These overlaps, along with staff movement, provide an opportunity to compare and contrast the different structures, policies and personalities engaged in joint planning.

Just such an opportunity existed, or had been created, in the East Anglian Region workshop on joint planning. The Region was following central government advice to review care in the community initiatives and the immediate relevance of the workshop was reflected in the applications; each of the participating authorities was represented. The conference was not conceived or organised by the Region but by participating authorities; it was funded by a grant from the Local Government Training Board.

Purpose of the workshop

The workshop was called against a background of an increasing knowledge of the barriers developing within the joint planning process and the need to develop a common agenda, or as the letter inviting attendance put it:

> There is a growing realisation that an adequate and appropriate package of care for elderly, mentally handicapped, mentally ill and physically handicapped clients can only be provided through a joint approach to care. This approach must involve both the statutory and the voluntary sectors, and the government's recent initiative concerning the discharge of patients from the long-term hospital in the community has been taken up with a variable degree of enthusiasm throughout the country. Initiatives in the East Anglian region have not been numerous but a number are developing and the workshop will:
>
> 1 review these initiatives and assess their contribution to care
> 2 review national developments in relation to the initiative
> 3 look at wider issues of community care and joint planning, especially in relation to formal and informal structures appropriate to joint planning
> 4 attempt to achieve a consensus concerning the likely developments in the region in the next five years and how these developments might be negotiated.
>
> The workshop should attract senior managers and planners from these organisations and agencies and will be run on a workshop/seminar basis, with opportunity for discussion of individual schemes and approaches. The emphasis will be on problem-solving rather than problem-generating.

The fourth objective of the workshop was ambitious and task-orientated. Its achievement depended significantly on the application of the Delphi technique, little used in the British public sector and still less in the field of personal care provision. The intention was to experiment with the technique to examine whether it could enhance – even in a short conference – development of an agreed agenda on joint services.

Finding an agreed agenda

A principal outcome of the workshop was hoped to be a new way in which the planning and coordination of community care could take place in the Region. By looking at the possible developments of community care over the longer term, participants might be able to identify immediate actions which would strengthen joint provision of services and set in motion longer-term developments. As a consequence of preliminary discussions about the nature of uncertainty and unknowability facing authorities engaged in the provision of health and social services, the authors decided to use alternative views of what the future might hold, in order to foster the kind of robust planning and analysis described above. The first step in such an exercise was to construct a set of alternative future states that participants would accept as not improbable and as meaningfully different. Having the participants themselves construct the alternative futures would, it was hoped, go a long way towards getting them accepted.

There are many techniques available which attempt to forecast future environmental changes. One of the best known is the Delphi survey. Delphi is an iterative technique devised to overcome reliance on individual intuitions about the future by enlisting a panel of informed people in a series of successive questionnaires, each constructed using the results of the previous questionnaire to provide controlled feedback. The survey entails respondents first proposing possible future changes and then, in subsequent rounds, judging the likelihood of the occurrence of those events, considering and reassessing their own individual responses in the light of the panel's collective response to the previous round. The technique has been characterised as organised brainstorming. Its purpose, however, is to foster eventual consensus about the future and this is not suitable for an exercise aimed at identifying probable alternative future states.

As used in the Ottawa-Carleton work, however, the Delphi technique can be modified after its first rounds to group respondents who have a propensity to agree on what changes are likely to occur. Each group thus exhibits a different, but similarly structured, view of what the future will hold. Subsequent rounds of the survey then refine descriptions of the groups' predicted futures, each of which in the end would be structured along similar dimensions.

Because the East Anglia workshop was scheduled as a two-day event, the multi-future planning exercise was intended only as a simulation of what could occur in local joint planning efforts. The exercise was designed as an interactive process in which workshop participants responded to the various rounds of survey questionnaires in between sessions devoted to discussions and addresses by outside speakers. Analysis of responses and design of the next rounds of the survey occurred during those sessions so that, by the end of the first day, rather crude alternative futures were developed which were used during the second day to 'plan' alternative courses of service development. Common elements of the resulting alternative courses of action would be the robust decisions which could form the agenda for immediate developments in joint community care.

Because of the fixed schedule of the workshop, then, the conduct of the survey, the construction of alternative futures, and the subsequent planning of robust short-term actions were all truncated into a timeframe much briefer than would be expected in a standard Delphi exercise. Of necessity, the analysis of results and the expected outputs – in terms of alternative future states and robust planning decisions – were recognised from the outset to be overly simple and certainly not prescriptive in their own rights. The purpose of the overall exercise, however, was not to come to decisions about what tasks to do, but rather – through a simulated joint planning effort – to explore what was hoped to be a more appropriate process for determining those tasks in the real life of joint planning in East Anglia.

Forecasting the future

In the first round of a standard Delphi survey, 'panel discussion' is initiated by asking participants to identify the future changes that they expect to occur in the environment within which their organisations operate. In the East Anglia workshop, each of the 23 participants were invited to list the three most significant changes in the environment which would affect joint planning over the next ten years. To help guide thinking and responses, five main areas of change were suggested: population, economics, government action, technology and professional practice.

After Round 1, the respondents' collective list of approximately 90 changes were edited into 33 change statements for the Round 2 questionnaire. The originally suggested changes were often stated in the form of causal links; these were separated into distinct statements. Duplicates were eliminated. Changes which were mere statements of hope rather than prediction were omitted.[1]

In Round 2 of the survey, which was conducted during the middle afternoon break of the first day, respondents were asked 'What is the likelihood that this change will occur during the next ten years?', for each of the 33 change statements. A seven-interval scale was used to solicit responses to the question, '1' being defined as 'impossible', '7' as 'virtually certain'.

Responses to the Round 2 questionnaire were analysed with the purpose of grouping respondents who had a propensity to agree on the likelihood of future changes. This grouping of respondents was done rapidly and consequently quite crudely. The Ottawa-Carleton work had entailed the use of computerised cluster analysis to group respondents. No such sophistication was attempted here. In this case, responses were reviewed manually to identify groups of respondents who might be said to share a similar 'world view'. This world view was judged on the basis of changes which would have widespread ramifications – such as the state of the economy, the level of resources devoted to health and social services, and political control at both national and local levels. Change statements which described technological breakthroughs or changes which could occur in relative isolation were not taken to be representative of world views.

Sketching alternative scenarios

As a result of this crude analysis, three groups of respondents were identified:

— group A, containing seven respondents, who tended to agree on a future which included continuing national economic decline, but maintenance of health and social service resources at current levels, and political instability at national level, but with increasing central control.

— group B, containing nine respondents, who tended to agree on a future which included a decline both in the national economy and in the resources commitments to health and social services, and a centre-right coalition at national political level which increasingly shifted responsibility for health service provision to local authorities.

— group C, containing seven respondents, who tended to agree on a future which included improved national economic performance and increased resource allocation to health and social services, and a coalition government at national level with heavy devolution to local authorities and health authorities.

Round 3 of the survey was conducted in the late afternoon of the first day as three separate exercises, in effect. Each respondent of each group received a questionnaire which was worded exactly as it was in Round 2, with the same one to seven scale. In this round, however, additional information was provided for each change statement. Each respondent was shown his or her previous response to the question of the likelihood of each of the 33 change statements, and the median response of his or her group (A, B or C). Thus each questionnaire was different and presented collective information separately for each of the three groups.

Respondents were asked to review each question and, after considering how their previous responses compared to those of their group, to indicate their reconsidered opinion on the likelihood of each change. The response of each group confirmed the general propensity to agree that had been identified after Round 2. Each group achieved near-consensus on the majority of change statements. The mean response of each group to each of the 33 change statements is shown in Note 1.

This information was synthesised during the evening of the first day in the writing of an environmental scenario for each group. In addition to the economic and governmental variables, the scenarios included projections of population patterns, professional practice and technology. For some variables, all three groups agreed – for example, each group predicted an increase in the proportion of the elderly population. But even for the non-world view variables, there were differences in expectation. Groups A and C, for example, projected stable urban populations, while group B expected these to decline. Groups B and C expected greater power to be exerted by consumers of services; group A did not.[2]

Planning robust actions

On the morning of the second day of the workshop, each group of participants was given the environmental scenario which emerged from its Delphi survey responses. Each group was asked to work collectively during the morning session and to do three things:

1 Review the scenario and identify its most significant opportunities and threats with respect to community health and social services.
2 Identify what would be the major strengths and weaknesses of current patterns of care and joint planning.
3 Develop agenda for action, which would capitalise on opportunities, parry threats, build on strengths and overcome weaknesses; the agenda were to be practical and related to developments in the environment, service, finance, organisation and management.

At the end of the group work, the three groups reconvened and reported on their progress. The analysis of strengths, weaknesses, opportunities and threats (sometimes referred to as 'SWOT analysis') was different, of course, for each group. For example, group A, which became characterised as the 'status quo' group because of its particular view of the future, saw a stable commitment to health and social service expenditure levels as an opportunity for advanced joint planning, but the accompanying threat of stronger central control might counter that. Group B, which foresaw 'bad times' ahead, saw the rise of consumerism and the accompanying emphasis on local or patch provision as a real strength, but declining health and social service expenditure levels might weaken the hand of joint planners. Group C, which held a 'rosy view' of the future, saw political devolution and increased resources as great opportunities, but worried that the likely increased complexity of joint planning and provision might not be able to take advantage of them.

Each group proposed a set of actions which should be taken now, given its own view of the future and the results of its analysis. Here, too, there were differences. For example, only group C, which foresaw increased revenue for health and social services, advocated the establishment of new multidisciplinary home care support teams and the development of new client/patient transportation systems. Groups A and B, neither of which foresaw increased revenue for health and social services, both advocated development of neighbourhood care.

The dilemma that faces planners of services in the real world is to gauge which actions, of the many open to them, are correct: new transportation systems or more neighbourhood care, for example. Will the future truly bring the increased resources (as group C thought) that will enable agencies to commit themselves to new developments now, or will resource levels actually drop (as group B thought), requiring cuts in existing services? One way in which planners try to determine which decision is 'best' is by asking 'Which future is most probable?' Another way, though, is to look for robust decisions by asking 'Which actions retain flexibility across a range of future commitments?' If we do not know precisely what the future will be, might we not focus on actions which probably are going to be helpful across a number of futures? Are there not things we can do now which will be needed and which will remain viable irrespective of the future?

This kind of 'robustness analysis' completed the simulated joint planning exercise at the workshop. Each group's agenda for action were compared across the five development areas: environment, service, finance, organisation and management. The comparisons are shown in Table 6.2.

Lessons learned

Clearly the service and financial implications of the groups' three futures were very different. Nonetheless, there were actions related

TABLE 6.2 Action agenda of groups A, B and C

Area	Group A	Group B	Group C
environment	educate politicians, public media mobilise care groups	increase political commitment inform clients/patients	inform clients/patients
service	develop neighbourhood care	increase neighbourhood care review institutional provision (to release resources)	develop multi-disciplinary home-care teams
finance	use issue-based finance revenue enhancement schemes use of private/voluntary services	use of private/voluntary services	reallocation to priority groups
organisation	develop better information networks	develop better information networks	develop better information networks develop transport systems more computers
	review/restructure joint planning	review joint planning machinery	review joint planning machinery
management		introduce incentives clarify responsibilities of managers	more accountable responsibilities
	interdisciplinary training	interdisciplinary training	interdisciplinary training

to other areas of development which all three groups saw as needed now. More politically aware and better informed consumers were regarded as an important objective in handling the environmental uncertainties facing joint planning. Accompanying this, on the organisational side, is the need to develop better information networks amongst joint planning agencies and to conduct a critical local review – and possible restructuring – of existing joint planning machinery. All three groups proposed similar actions on the organisational front. All three groups also proposed that training of officers and members, particularly with regard to clarifying respective responsibilities, is an important action that is needed now.

There were other proposed actions that were common to two of the three groups. For example, groups A and B both advocated more active campaigning to gain increased political commitment to health and social services. Such action, were it to be taken, might be useful now, but could prove unnecessary (or even politically harmful) should the future envisaged by group C materialise. In this way the robustness analysis also helps to identify the risk of actions taken now should an unfavourable future occur. But its more obvious benefit is in helping identify those actions that are truly robust – and that will be so irrespective of the future.

The robust environmental, organisational and managerial actions which emerged from the workshop exercise may seem obvious, but they appear obvious now only after the fact. Open discussions amongst the participants about what to do next in joint planning easily would have been bogged down in arguments about their different perceptions – not only about the shape of the future, but also about the types of services needed, about expenditure, and about organisational objectives. But in spite of these differences in East Anglia, there is commonality: there is a recognition of need for more informed consumers, for example, for better information, and for better training. The workshop began by recognising the impossibility of predicting whose different views would prevail and went on to incorporate those differences in a simulated joint planning process. By doing that, it enabled participants to construct an agreed and robust agenda for action that they could all support.

References

Best, G; Parston, G; and Rosenhead, J (1986), 'Robustness in Practice – The Regional Planning of Health Services', *Journal of the Operational Research Society* (37)5 pp 463–78.

Notes

1 The following questionnaire was used:

Developments in care in the community and joint planning

The futures of joint planning

Average responses — groups A, B, and C

What is the likelihood that this change will occur during the next ten years?

1 — impossible
7 — virtually certain

A, B, C — mean response of group
(Please circle answer)

---

1   There will be a growth in the proportion of the elderly population

1	2	3	4	5	6	7
						A
						B
						C

2   People will live longer

1	2	3	4	5	6	7
					B	A
					C	

3   There will be more dependent people living in the community

1	2	3	4	5	6	7
					A	C
					B	

4   The rate of mental illness will increase

1	2	3	4	5	6	7
			C	B	A	

5   Housing will become less available

1	2	3	4	5	6	7
			B		A	
			C			

6   Urban populations will decline in number

1	2	3	4	5	6	7
			A	B		
			C			

7   Urban populations will be poorer

1	2	3	4	5	6	7
			C	A		
				B		

8   The national north/south economic divide will be magnified

1	2	3	4	5	6	7
				A	B	
				C		

9   There will be many more unemployed people

1	2	3	4	5	6	7
	C				A	
					B	

10   Nationally, the economy will decline

1	2	3	4	5	6	7
	C			A		
				B		

11   Nationally, the economy will remain as it is

1	2	3	4	5	6	7
		A				
		B				
		C				

12   Nationally, the economy will improve

1	2	3	4	5	6	7
		A			C	
		B				

13   Public sector expenditure on health and social services will decline

1	2	3	4	5	6	7
	C	A			B	

14   Public sector expenditure on health and social services will grow

1	2	3	4	5	6	7
	B			A	C	

15   The government will support private sector growth in health and social services

1	2	3	4	5	6	7
				C	A	
					B	

16   The voluntary sector will expand

1	2	3	4	5	6	7
				A	B	
					C	

17   The Conservatives will be in government

1	2	3	4	5	6	7
		A	B			
		C				

18   The SDP/Alliance will be in government

1	2	3	4	5	6	7
	C	A	B			

19   Labour will be in government

1	2	3	4	5	6	7
		A				
		B				
		C				

20   There will be a coalition government

1	2	3	4	5	6	7
	A		B	C		

21   There will be increasing government control from the centre

1	2	3	4	5	6	7
			B	A		
			C			

22   There will be greater devolution to local and health authorities

1	2	3	4	5	6	7
			A	C		
			B			

23   Local authorities and health authorities will be merged

1	2	3	4	5	6	7
	C		A	B		

24   Consensus management will return

1	2	3	4	5	6	7
		B	A			
		C				

25   Consumers will demand more from statutorily provided services

1	2	3	4	5	6	7
				A	B	
				C		

26   Consumers will exert more influence on service provision

1	2	3	4	5	6	7
			A	B	C	

27   Professional demarcation and training will be more specialised

1	2	3	4	5	6	7
			A	B		
			C			

28   The number of trained professionals will decline

1	2	3	4	5	6	7
		A	B			
		C				

29 More service resources will be devoted to new technologies

1	2	3	4	5	6	7
			A	C		
			B			

30 Use of high technologies will be concentrated on specific client/patient groups

1	2	3	4	5	6	7
				A	B	
					C	

31 High speed information systems will be in use more generally

1	2	3	4	5	6	7
					A	C
					B	

32 There will be computerised information exchange between authorities

1	2	3	4	5	6	7
			A		B	C

33 There will be computerised home surveillance of individuals with special needs

1	2	3	4	5	6	7
				A	B	
					C	

2 The following scenarios were given:

Scenario A

Population

There will be an increase in the proportion of the elderly population, many of whom will live longer. This will contribute to more dependent people living in the community, being supported by a smaller income-earning proportion of the population, as unemployment will increase significantly. Mental illness will increase.

In urban areas, whilst the population will remain about the same size as it is currently, average income will fall, and housing will be in short supply.

Economy

The economy will decline, and the north/south divide will be magnified. Public expenditure on health and social services, however, will not be cut. The roles of the private and voluntary sectors will expand.

Government action

There will be some political instability, with no party emerging as a strong government. However, central government will exert increasing control, with little devolution to localities.

Local authorities and health authorities will remain independent organisations. Consumers will demand more from statutorily provided services, but will not exert increased influence over authorities.

Professional practice and technology

Patterns of professional practice will remain largely unchanged.

More money will be spent on new technologies, with the use of high technologies concentrated on specific client and patient groups. This will include computerised home surveillance.

Whilst high speed information systems will be in use more generally, there will not be computerised information exchanges between authorities.

Scenario B

Population

There will be an increase in the proportion of the elderly population, many of whom will live longer. This will contribute to more dependent people living in the community, being supported by a smaller income-earning proportion of the population, as unemployment will increase significantly. Mental illness will increase.

In urban areas, the population will decline in number and will be poorer.

Economy

The economy will decline, and the north/south divide will be magnified. Public expenditure on health and social services will be cut significantly. The roles of private and voluntary sectors will expand.

Government action

There will be an SDP/Alliance/Conservative coalition in government. Whilst central control will not increase, neither will levels of local responsibility. However, local authorities will increasingly assume responsibility for health services provision, now held by health authorities.

Consumers will demand more from statutorily provided services and their power to influence local and national decisions will increase.

Professional practice and technology

Patterns of professional practice will remain largely unchanged, although the number of trained professionals will decline slightly.

More money will be spent on new technologies, with the use of high technology concentrated on specific client and patient groups. This will include computerised home surveillance.

High speed information systems will be in use more generally, and there will be computerised information exchange between authorities.

Scenario C

Population

There will be an increase in the proportion of the elderly population, many of whom will live longer. This will contribute to more dependent people living in the community.

In urban areas, the population will remain about the same size as it is currently.

Economy

Although the north/south divide will be magnified, the national economy will improve significantly, and unemployment will fall. As a consequence, public expenditure on health and social services will be increased, even though the roles of private and voluntary sectors also will expand.

Government action

There will be a coalition government, with no single party able to exert leadership. Central government controls will give way to devolved responsibilities to local and health authorities, which will remain independent organisations.

Consumers will demand more from statutorily provided services and their power to influence local and national decisions will increase.

Professional practice and technology

Patterns of professional practice will remain largely unchanged.

More money will be spent on new technologies, with the use of high technologies concentrated on specific client and patient groups. This will include computerised home surveillance.

High speed information systems will be in use more generally, and there will be computerised information exchanges between authorities.

7 Building information bridges

Rob Ballantyne and David Symes

Introduction

Preceding chapters have demonstrated some of the difficulties which exist in attempting to achieve collaboration between health and local authorities, and indeed some of the successes that have been achieved. Some of the difficulties encountered can be related to the lack of a common vocabulary (exemplified by the failure to resolve the 'client/patient' description of the customer), others to different styles of implementing change which resulted in an absence of agreed critical success factors. The increasing use of information techniques and new technology by managers in both sectors can assist in resolving some of these current differences.

Information is often viewed as a neutral resource and indeed as a resource which costs nothing. Whilst clearly this is not strictly true, it often proves so difficult to identify the cost of collection, storage and interpretation that the two sides of the divide could perhaps accept it as a joint resource, particularly where common programmes are identified. The development of joint information systems, however, requires an explicit statement of objectives and values. The difficulties that arise from the different world views of, for example, doctors and social workers, are well-known. There is a danger that different professions peer at each other suspiciously, using stereotypes which more often manifest themselves in private conversations than they do in discussions of the joint consultative committees.

In addition to these differences in values, however, there are major differences in political, financial and organisational structures which make joint working hard to achieve.

To what extent could information and new technology help to build bridges? It is argued here that by systematically developing common information approaches, a start can be made in developing a common language within which the issues of values and priorities can be identified. The development of information systems, particularly those involving new technology, do involve explicit statements of objectives and values. The development of shared information will force to the forefront the need to confront differences in management style and organisational values.

It is a fact of life that many of the information systems that exist, in both local and health authorities, work from the top down. They are designed to feed the information requirements of, for instance, the Department of Health and Social Security. 'DHSS Returns' are a feature of life in both authorities and are a common element of bureaucratic work. It is therefore all the more regrettable that little effort appears to have been made at central government level to coordinate the information demanded to enable a clearer picture of, for instance, the progress in community care, to be developed.

Considerable work has been carried out within the NHS to look systematically at information requirements. The best-known example of this is the work of the Korner Committee whose recommendations have transformed NHS information systems.

The Korner work has been followed by other initiatives in the NHS, including the use of data modelling and the development of 'information strategies' based on explicit statements of 'business objectives'. However, little regard is being paid to the need to ease joint planning and joint working, particularly with regard to services for elderly people and those with mental or physical handicaps or mental illness.

One consequence of this is that there is a grave lack of 'follow through' information systems which can trace the progress of individuals in community care. In fact few if any systems allow what happens to the individuals, supposedly the beneficiaries of community care policies, to be established. Thus the Audit Commission in its major review of community care, was able to observe that 'it must be a matter of grave concern that although there are 37,000 fewer mentally ill and mentally handicapped patients today than there were ten years ago, no one knows what has happened to many of those who were discharged'. It went on to note that some would have died; others are likely to be in some form of residential care; the rest should be receiving support in the community. Many, however, have been before the courts, are in prison or have become vagrants or wanderers.

Proper follow through systems would allow the monitoring of what has happened to such people, and therefore make it easier to revise or fine-tune policies accordingly. The implications, however, would be that such systems would be people-based, not event-based. They would also be dynamic rather than static in as much as they would need to measure 'flows' and not just 'stocks'.

There would thus be a need for a realignment of current systems, which are mainly static and event- rather than people-based.

The history of information development in organisations

The history of organisational responses to information technology has been to worry first about the boxes or hardware, then about the money, followed by the software systems, then the human systems, and finally the organisation's values and objectives. If an organisation is to be effective it should tackle these issues in reverse order. For effective collaboration between two organisations, it is important to take stock of the degree of organisational maturity, ensure that both are clear about their objectives and values and then start to talk about the information required by each at all levels to deliver a service to the customer.

The history of most organisations' use of information technology follows a well-trodden path of reacting to what, at various stages of evolution, appears to be the major problem needing to be confronted. Eventually organisations realise that the last problem to be confronted is at the same time the most crucial and difficult to deal with, and as such should have been the first to be considered instead of the last. These stages are detailed below to assist in the later assessment of where health and local authorities are on this evolutionary path, so that local partnerships can jointly establish the sense of concentrating on the major question at an early stage rather than avoiding this by trying to resolve their information strategies in isolation.

The initial set of questions which organisations face when striving to resolve an information technology strategy are: what *hardware* should be purchased, should the organisation standardise, and if so should it standardise on one manufacturer's range or on two manufacturers' ranges? At this stage much time and effort is devoted to achieving an understanding of the potential and immediate benefits of automating information handling. After much deliberation a choice will be made of the boxes to be used to process this quantity of data. The organisation, however, has only begun to interact with the wider issues of the information revolution and many more issues will require its attention before a mature organisation emerges.

The second aspect of the information revolution to be faced by most organisations consists of finding the *money* to allow their initial purchases to grow, as more data is required to be retained without slowing down processing speeds, particularly where transaction processing is involved. The next major decision taken by an organisation is therefore the extent of its budget to invest in information technology.

The third step is to decide on *software languages or packages*. It is at this stage that the organisation begins to question what the computers and associated investment are really for. Having decided on the software environment in which new systems will be written, organisations then become aware of the next problem associated with the information revolution which needs to be addressed.

This fourth issue facing the organisation is the *human system* which the computers and software are intended to serve. There are many facets to the problems associated with successfully suiting people to machines and machine-based systems. Some of these problems are to do with machine phobia; some are due to the discomfort managers feel when pictures of their performance (ie 'information') are presented to them, particularly where the picture of what is in fact happening is at odds with their intuitive 'feel' for events.

In the face of such discomfort, a hierarchy of responses has been observed. The first response is to attempt to discredit the data. The second response involves questioning the techniques used to acquire, classify or interpret the data. The third response is to accept that the picture was true but because of action already taken is no longer so. The fourth response is to argue that the action required to deal with the situation is outside the short-term control of the manager and that long-term investment in people or buildings is necessary. When none of these responses is applicable, the result is an admission that the information has illuminated something of the complex process of delivering care which the manager was unaware of but, in the light of this evidence, will investigate.

Arising out of this sort of experience of individuals with information systems, a sufficient number of employees will begin to question whether the information which is being routinely collected and analysed is appropriate to the role of the organisation. Might there be too much irrelevant data and not sufficient real information related to the core values and objectives of the organisation? It is at this stage of responding to the information revolution that mature organisations emerge with clearly stated objectives and core values, along with explicit statements of the management style and skills, or 'culture', which is best suited to delivering the service required.

Information use in organisations

Organisations can be described as systems for the collection, storage, interpretation and presentation of information about products. Both health and local authorities exist to deliver a product called 'care'. The customers of both organisations are often the same individuals. Both organisations therefore spend much of their time and money processing information about the needs and demands of the same individual customers and the extent to which the service provided to them corresponds to their requirements. The result of such activity is often the identification of shortfalls in resources or of different ways in which existing resources could be used to provide a more appropriate service.

Similar processes exist within both health and local authority organisations. Both organisations comply with the model of information-processing needs of organisations shown in Figure 7.1.

The base of the pyramid represents the delivery of service to individuals on a day to day basis. The information requirements of the operational level of an organisation are termed 'transaction processing'. An example of this in the health service is the patient administration system in most hospitals, which amongst other uses produces labels for use by diagnostic departments and wards to speed up the identification of test requests and results for individual patients.

Within social services these processes are less frequently computerised. Many departments keep their basic records of clients or contacts on manual index systems, although there is increasing use of computerised systems. Even within health services the domiciliary services such as health visiting and district nursing are much less computerised than are the major hospital systems.

Transaction processing systems require expensive mainframe computers to process data about a large potential customer base, only a small proportion of which is in direct contact with the organisation at any one time. The failure of such a system to deliver is felt immediately and the consequences of breakdown unsettles the operational staff concerned. Because of this day to day dependence of operational staff on transaction processing systems, the data which they store is often very accurate.

The level of the organisational pyramid above the operational level is the operational management level of an organisation, whose needs relate less to individual customers and staff and more to aggregates. The corresponding information system which this level requires is termed a management information system. The questions which such systems answer best are what service was provided, where did it happen, who received/provided the service and how often and when was the service provided? The people who ask these questions most often are the heads of departments who must balance out resource availability and service demands on a daily basis, often by adjusting rotas, assessing priorities or deciding on the relative urgency of cases of individual customers on waiting lists.

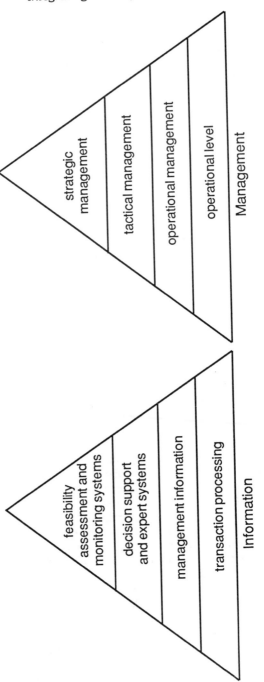

FIGURE 7.1   Information and management – finding the right levels

The third tier of the organisational pyramid is the tactical management level, which can be represented by district health authorities and corresponding local authority departments such as social services, housing, education and environmental health. This level of an organisation requires information systems which manipulate aggregated data to answer questions such as where else, when else and how else can the service be provided, what else should be provided and who else should receive/provide the service? Such questions require the availability of decision support systems which enable tactical decisions to be modelled and implications of alternative courses of action to be assessed prior to deliberation. It is at this level that performance review systems are also used to assess the relative efficiency, effectiveness and economy with which existing resources are used compared with other service providers. The DHSS Performance Indicator Package and Local Authority Comparisons produced annually by CIPFA (Chartered Institute of Public Finance Accountants) are examples of this information requirement. Arising out of the use of performance review systems by this tier, organisations are beginning to develop expert systems which incorporate the judgements of performance reviewers so that their relatively expensive knowledge can be used widely and relatively cheaply.

The final tier of the organisational pyramid is concerned with strategic management and can be represented by regional health authorities and the local authorities (as distinct from their constituent departments). It is this tier which is concerned with long-term decisions on where the organisation as a whole is heading and what level of resources will be required over future years to achieve these objectives. This tier is often less concerned with the efficiency with which elements of the organisation use resources to meet the needs of customers, as with which elements should exist at all. In the health service this takes the form of facility planning which concentrates on the long-term development of new hospitals and the corresponding closure or rationalisation of existing facilities. In local authorities the equivalent is the manifesto commitments of political parties, which record the priorities to be accorded in the future to the various local government departments. The information requirements of this tier are related to the assessment of the feasibility of statements of organisational values.

Theory applied to health and local authorities

The one area where potentially it should be possible for health and local authorities to reach common accord is the identification of major objectives and, hopefully, core values (particularly because their respective customers are often the same individuals), though this is often difficult in practice. Following on from this stage, both organisations need to examine the human systems which they have available to them for meeting their objectives and then examine the software systems available for providing employees with the information needed to deliver the service to their customers. After these issues have been jointly examined it will be appropriate to negotiate what money is required for the human and software systems, and how much should be contributed from each, before deciding which make of computers need be purchased. As preceding chapters have demonstrated, this is far from the current pattern of joint working between authorities. The remainder of this chapter takes stock of the patchy experience to date of information system development within both sectors and applies these experiences to the theory expounded above.

Examining the distinct organisational levels in turn will provide a framework within which readers will be able to place their own organisation and, as developments occur, identify where gaps may need to be addressed.

The operational level

Within health authorities, as a result of the recent implementation of radical proposals to collect data of use primarily at the operational level (the Korner Working Group Proposals), most hospitals now make use of a patient administration system as a daily administrative aid to patient care. These systems help with the registration of patients; booking of outpatient clinics and appointments; producing labels for use by wards and diagnostic departments; theatre lists; waiting lists for admission, and booking of ambulances for future hospital visits. At the time of registration various data items are requested to assist other management levels to discharge their responsibilities. These items include codes for the area of residence, for diagnosis and for surgical interventions. By aggregating these and other data items, the management information system (or the patient information system) is established in such a way that the accuracy of data is high and separate software can be used to analyse and interpret what service has been provided in the previous month(s).

The existence of registers within local authorities is widespread but the tendency is for these to record customer details and occasional details of services required, but rarely includes a history of interventions suitable for further analysis. A number of such registers are required by statute and have not been enhanced to do other than meet statutory requirements. Other locally developed registers will build on the data required by the operational levels, but there has been little attempt to collect a minimum data set across all authorities as has occurred with the health service. The absence of such minimum data sets limits the use of data held on registers, as they are incapable of assisting in the comparison of relative performance.

Registers are in use by some health authorities particularly in the fields of services for people with mental illness or mental handicap. The production of joint registers is often delayed because of problems associated with ownership and confidentiality. The wider use of joint registers, however, offers major opportunities for overcoming the lack of a partnership between health and local authorities.

Operational management levels

The provision of feedback on peaks and troughs on a daily basis to heads of departments or field teams is an area where neither health nor local authorities have generated much information of immediate use. Any joint ventures in the future, therefore, would do well to address the needs of such people, particularly as there is unlikely to be a history of commitment to existing systems which staff might find difficult to manage without.

Tactical management levels

In recent years most public services have found it necessary to collect and analyse data about efficiency, effectiveness and economy as elements of the introduction of modern management to public services. By and large the relative ease with which data about these aspects of performance can be collected means that insufficient attention is given to collecting data relating to customer satisfaction: professionally defined measures of quality of care and even relative access or treatment intensity rates. There is much that all branches of public service can learn from responses to the introduction of modern management techniques in recent years, but even more can be learnt by discussing jointly how to go beyond modern management to measure adequately many of the softer aspects of performance. Failure to achieve this will result in the alienation of professional staff, who will resent being treated as technicians. This is a matter of relevance for the next two to three years across all areas of public service. There is therefore much to be gained by sharing experiences and concerns across the health and local authority divide. Means of capturing data which professionals feel indicates aspects of their performance relating to quality and consumer satisfaction, will be needed in both sectors if the respective organisations are to face up to this aspect of the information revolution without widening the gulf that already exists between managers and professionals.

The development of decision support systems using integrated software packages is an area where it will be relatively easy for both sectors to work together. This will be particularly so if the models draw on existing databases within each organisation but integrate them by use of indices of change over time to illustrate relative movements of resources such as manpower finance and space or buildings. Figure 7.2, on the strategic path of the elderly programme for Trent Regional Health Authority, illustrates how this could be possible.

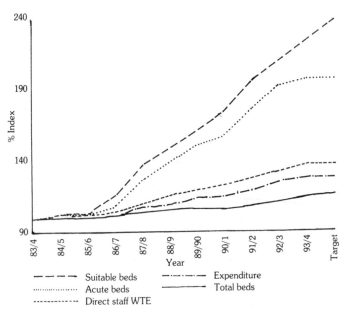

FIGURE 7.2   Strategic path of elderly programme

Source: Trent Regional Health Authority

The strategic levels

The NHS management board is beginning to address the need to develop methodologies for ensuring that long-term (ie 10-year) plans are feasible from the outset and that annual programmes are used to monitor the achievement or otherwise of intended growth rates for manpower finance and activity. A system called the management accounting framework allows the feasibility of annual programmes to be assessed against long-term plans. One aspect of this approach is to record the relative shifts in the pattern locally of health and local authority provision for people with mental handicap. As the piecharts in Figure 7.3 show, there is a wide variation between districts in terms of the eventual pattern of joint service to be provided, which is a reflection of different degrees of success with joint planning. There is also an indication of different rates of progress, depending on the pace of change of local authority plans, which tend to be more pragmatic than those of the associated health authority. This difference in approaches to development of services has dogged many attempts to plan sensibly. Getting the information to show the patterns of service geographically, and then using that information, is one way of bringing the approaches together. At a minimum the consequences of not working jointly, in terms of excessive provision of inappropriate care, can be seen.

Joint monitoring and planning for services for people with mental handicap

The joint objective of services for people with mental handicap should be to achieve a situation where all such people receive a service which is appropriate to their individual needs. This requires information about their needs and joint assessments of possible alternative models or packages of care. Running in parallel with this are the changes in resource allocation and use which are implied by the products of individual plans.

Some authorities have started to develop their services based on jointly run mental handicap registers. These registers seek to identify all of the relevant people within a catchment area and normally categorise their characteristics and needs. They are an example of jointly run 'person-based' information systems. Their existence provides information for both the operational/transactional level of the model and the management/management information level. Because it proves difficult to link the two levels effectively, when the register is useful for management purposes the data can become rapidly out of date. A register which is created for operational reasons may often not be structured in such a way as to allow data to be manipulated for management and planning purposes.

The development of joint registers can be a positive catalyst to addressing the important question of definitions, which can in turn only be resolved if the underlying values of both organisations are

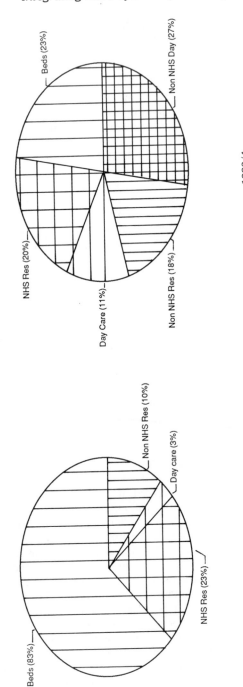

FIGURE 7.3 Mental handicap – different service patterns

Mental Handicap Facilities
Authority Two

Beds (23%)
Non NHS Day (27%)
NHS Res (20%)
Day Care (11%)
Non NHS Res (18%)
1993/4

Mental Handicap Facilities
Authority One

Non NHS Res (10%)
Day care (3%)
NHS Res (23%)
Beds (83%)
1993/4

considered. For example, 'Who are the customers?' and 'How should a good or appropriate service be defined and measured?'.

The role of a joint database of personal needs for service is to provide a baseline of the current situation on which planning can be based empirically. Jointly owned information can help in such a debate. Whilst a number of authorities have approached planning in this way, few have yet achieved the translation of this level of analysis into longer-term, monitorable plans.

The reasons for this failure to produce monitorable plans lie in the differences in the structure, style, values, strategies, systems and skills of health and local authorities. The purpose of this chapter is to suggest some of the mechanisms which might be used to monitor and provide feedback on progress towards strategic aims, and to evaluate the extent to which such aims remain appropriate or attainable.

Assuming a strategic target of, say, 75% of all individuals being appropriately cared for within 10 years of a joint plan, it will be possible to monitor the different progress of health authority and local authority resource shifts along the lines of the graph in Figure 7.4.

These graphs will be produced annually following a reassessment by the local professionals of the number of customers who are appropriately cared for. This approach will enable staff to collect information of use to tactical and strategic management levels as a by-product of operational transaction processing systems used by both authorities to record details of individual customers and their needs for service, along with a summary of services provided. Such a record in use by Redbidge Health Authority is reproduced in Figure 7.5 and can form the basis of an information system of value to all levels of both authorities.

Lessons learned and signposts

The failures of joint planning in the past have been exacerbated by the exercise, by both sectors, of 'skilled incompetence': managerial behaviour in which points of view are put in a manner that avoids giving offence to others or 'rocking the boat', thus ensuring the failure to resolve underlying problems. This state of affairs results in an inability to confront the truth, which leads in due course to communication gaps and defensive coverups.

The implications of reviewing the information systems of organisations can facilitate turning the tide of skilled incompetence by confronting underlying problems and sharing values, thus resolving communication gaps. Joint development of follow through and

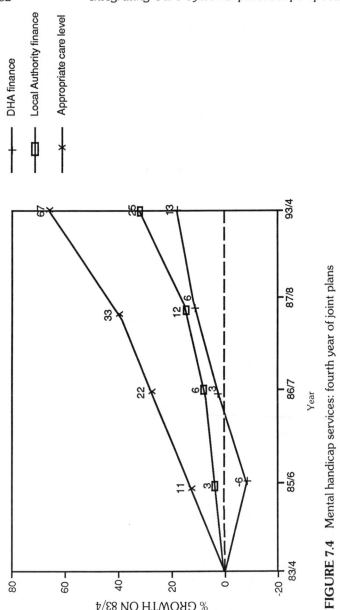

FIGURE 7.4   Mental handicap services: fourth year of joint plans

INDIVIDUAL SUMMARY SHEET

Hospital TV	Personal number: A/234/8	W.F. Group 3
Date of Birth 121106	Sex f	Admission Date: 430127

Day Care Code 6	Involved Party Siblings	Links n
	Contact (frequency) = 2 Contact (extent) = 3	
Relatives Views 99	Residents Views 0	Friends n

EXTRACTS FROM NATIONAL
DEVELOPMENT ASSESSMENT

Continence Score	= 3
Mobility Score	= 3
Behavioural Score	= 3
Self Help Score	= 2
Visual Score	= 3
Hearing Ability	= 3
Use of Speech	= 3
Epilepsy Extent	= 3
Chronic Physical Disorder	= 1

NDT SCORE	Old NDT SCORE
2	1

FIGURE 7.5   Individual summary sheet

transaction processing systems which feed management information systems, decision support systems and expert systems, as well as feasibility monitoring systems, is possible and is perhaps the best way of overcoming the divide between the two sectors. This is because information technology eventually forces mature organisations to state explicitly their objectives and core values and, in the light of this, to define the human systems and information systems needed to deliver a good service to their customers. This, after all, is how we should judge the success or otherwise of joint planning.

References

Korner Committee: Reports on the Steering Group on Health Services Information (Chairman – Mrs E Korner), London, NHS DHSS 1982.
Making a Reality of Community Care – a report by the Audit Commission for England and Wales, London, HMSO 1980.

8 Learning from the care in the community initiative

Judy Renshaw and Corinne Thomason

The care in the community initiative aims to promote alternative forms of care for people in long-stay hospitals. A series of government-sponsored pilot projects, developed as part of the initiative, form an attempt to encourage experimentation in service delivery. They are the focus of this chapter. The authors are in the privileged position of having known the projects from their inception and early operation. The following material owes much to project personnel who took the time to share their experiences with us. It also relates our own perceptions of what we have seen, heard and read during the evaluation.

We begin with a general overview of the birth of the initiative, the characteristics of the projects and the role of Personal Social Services Research Unit (PSSRU) as evaluator, then proceed to highlight a number of issues which have arisen as plans have been translated into action.

The initiative

The government's care in the community initiative was first proposed in a 1981 consultative document[1] and consolidated in the 1983 DHSS circular HC(83)6.[2] It was specifically aimed at helping long-stay hospital patients to live in alternative settings in the community, where this would be best for them and is what they and their families prefer.

The initiative was in step with recent trends towards de-institutionalisation, dealing as it did with those already in hospital rather than preventing new admissions. It added a further impetus to a policy of community care which had rather run out of steam, and encouraged experimentation, a somewhat unusual feature of social policy in this country.

The legislation it introduced was intended to overcome previous barriers to change, by enabling a transfer of responsibility and resources from health authorities to other organisations. NHS resources could be transferred directly, either in the form of lump sums or grants, to local authorities and other agencies for as long as necessary to provide community care for long-stay patients moved from hospital. The circular also offered a stimulus to joint planning by extending joint finance arrangements to cover housing and education as well as social services.

In addition, a total sum of about £19m (at 1986 prices) was added to joint finance funds over five years for a programme of pilot projects. The programme was intended to launch the initiative and to explore and evaluate different approaches to moving people and resources into community care, intended to be both beneficial to the client and cost-effective, the results of which could then be disseminated widely.

Health and local authorities were invited to submit proposals worked out locally, although the care could be provided by either statutory or voluntary agencies. Projects had to meet certain criteria; for example, needs had to be specified and assessed in advance and the wishes of patients and their families taken into account. The circular stipulated that projects should be developed jointly by health and local authority personnel, possibly involving voluntary organisations and endorsed by the joint consultative committee (JCC). There also had to be an undertaking that the project would continue with local funding once central funding had ceased.

The selection of projects aimed to achieve a broad spread geographically and among different kinds of disability, as well as to support promising proposals. In total, more than 250 proposals were received from around the country.

The pilot projects

Twenty eight projects were selected, each funded for three years. There were two rounds: thirteen projects started in April 1984 and fifteen started a year later. Twelve projects are for mentally handicapped people, eight for mentally ill people, seven for the elderly and elderly mentally infirm people and one is for physically handicapped people. Together, the 28 pilot projects aim to move about 1100 long-stay patients into the community.

There is a tremendous variety of community provision within the pilot project programme. Some have introduced new models of care and others have replicated previously tried versions. They cater for people who need different degrees of support and care and include residential care, day care provision and support services for patients' families. Some aim to provide for very small numbers of people – as few as three – and others will care for over 100. The larger projects are generally able to provide a more comprehensive range of services from within their own resources. Smaller projects tend to rely more heavily on those provided elsewhere. Each project also utilises a range of funds from other sources, such as supplementary benefit, joint finance and mainstream agencies.

Role of the PSSRU

The PSSRU, at the University of Kent at Canterbury, was commissioned to promote the care in the community initiative and to monitor and evaluate the pilot projects. One of the major reasons for the incorporation of a monitoring and evaluation exercise into the eventual care in the community pilot scheme was the concern expressed by both the Public Accounts Committee and DHSS about the need to monitor the use of joint finance and to review the cost-effectiveness of community care.

The PSSRU has a multiple role which incorporates the tasks of promotion, monitoring and evaluation. The activities are diverse and not necessarily complementary, although there are areas of overlap.

In the early days much effort was expended on promotion and development work. As the programme has gathered momentum the evaluation proper has begun; clients and staff are being interviewed and records completed. But rather than diminishing, monitoring and developmental activities have assumed greater prominence. They 'have grown like Topsy' both in and outside the programme. The delays which many projects have encountered have, in turn, allowed us more time for these activities, although we are increasingly bound by a timetable for data collection, analysis and evaluation. Our promotion, monitoring and evaluation tasks are described briefly below and summarised in Boxes 1–3.

Promotion

Providing information about the initiative has become a far more significant activity than was originally envisaged. The aims are to publicise the initiative, disseminate information about what is happening and describe some of the early developments in the demonstration projects. Activities include the production of newsletters, participation in seminars, advice on the production of a video, and other written outputs. The establishment of an information exchange, facilitated by regular conferences, was emphasised at an early stage. It was intended to provide support for project managers and workers who might otherwise become isolated within their own schemes; new ideas could be introduced and problems more easily overcome. A further aim of the exchange was to provide ideas and information for groups outside the programme of pilot projects. In practice it has also greatly assisted our monitoring task.

Monitoring

The original intention was quite simply to record the progress of the projects and describe what was happening to a wider audience, although this role has also expanded.

We decided to make a general distinction between monitoring and evaluation activities. The information collected in monitoring is more often routinely available from projects by virtue of its being necessary for their own use. The timescale of collection, analysis/synthesis and dissemination of information is much shorter and is, therefore, better able to be assimilated by schemes and used

---

Publicity

1 Seminars to drum up support for the initiative.

2 Production of a video.

3 Production of biannual newsletters.

4 Organisation and hosting of biannual conferences for project personnel.

5 Participation in a regular series of DHSS seminars to publicise the initiative.

6 Information exchange and advice to LA/HA officers, professionals and other researchers.

7 Compilation of a research directory.

8 Speaking at other conferences here and abroad.

9 Organisation of countrywide roadshows to publicise the initiative.

10 Various written outputs, articles, book chapters, books.

BOX 1

Monitoring

1   To describe what is happening to the rest of the world, in effect to tell the story of the pilot projects.

2   To ensure that projects abide by the terms of the circular, eg long-stay patients, moving people from hospital.

3   To ensure that projects transfer the agreed number of clients and to chart their progress and record ultimate destinations.

4   To attend meetings when required.

5   In certain circumstances to advise.

6   To encourage the use of the case review procedure as a practice tool.

7   To provide information for projects.

BOX 2

to influence practice. This brings monitoring close to an evaluation model often described as 'action research'. Evaluation activity is more likely to be based on a clear theoretical framework from which questions will be designed to test hypotheses. Monitoring information tends to be designed in order to meet practical and immediate needs.

The monitoring was to proceed at two levels. First it was intended to make use of information regularly supplied by projects (including the initial application, annual reports of progress and data about client numbers and expenditure incurred). In practice it also entails regular visiting of the projects, the organisation of conferences and workshops for them and the provision of regular reports to the DHSS.

On a second level it was hoped to obtain a more detailed account of the progress of each project. This meant, at least, interviewing project managers and other key individuals at intervals about their activities and the particular challenges which they face. This is where we found that monitoring and evaluation activities do overlap and that the two can complement each other. Much of the 'Process' side of our evaluation (described below) fits more snugly into our monitoring activities; for example, narrative reports of meetings, focused interviews and descriptions of care plans of a qualitative nature. One very important element has been the promotion of case review systems, which are similar to the 'individual programme plans' now widely used in relation to people with mental handicaps. These, can provide useful information for both practice and research.

Our special relationship with projects has sometimes led to unanticipated requests for advice, on matters of practice, for instance. Although the nature of our involvement in the programme has meant that we have accumulated information about ways of tackling certain problems, we are not in a position to give practice advice. In these cases our policy has been to relate the experiences of other projects, put people in touch with one another, or with the appropriate person in the DHSS, and liaise with the DHSS if necessary.

Evaluation

The evaluative role of the PSSRU is constrained by the number of projects, their geographical spread and the different client groups involved.

The research is funded as an integral part of the programme, although its perspective is independent from the management of the initiative. The intention to influence policy was always on the agenda and it was agreed that use could be made of the monitoring information to add to the evaluation and subsequent policy recommendations.

Our central research task was to discover:

In what circumstances can cost-effective community services be provided to meet the needs of particular groups of long-stay hospital patients.

And to address this we determined to ask of each project:

1 Does it improve the well-being of clients?
2 What does it cost?
3 How does it work?

The strategy we have pursued, therefore, is to adopt a modular research framework in the sense that not all parts of it will be relevant to all of the projects. It is deliberately constructed at a level of generality which makes it suitable for the programme as a whole rather than for a particular scheme, and it can be modified accordingly for individual projects. The main focus of our research effort is inevitably on a limited range of topics within the framework. To collect more detailed information about these and other topics we depend heavily on the interest and participation of the projects themselves. To this end we have gone to considerable lengths to consult projects and others in the field. We also aimed to develop some instruments which are useful to projects themselves. An example of this is the case review form, mentioned earlier.

Some additional studies have been developed locally which are more focused and more detailed than the PSSRU approach – which is programme-based – could afford to be. These special evaluations have provided useful controls for our own research.

The broad framework of the investigation can be subdivided into four topics: outcomes, costs, process and services in practice. Box 3 outlines the information we are collecting in each category. The general topics are derived from the production of a welfare model.[3] This is an analogy to the economic theory of production which has been developed in the PSSRU to take into account all aspects of the process of providing welfare services and their consequences. It describes as 'inputs' both resources such as buildings and staff, and non-resources such as regime and management procedures, and characteristics of clients. Both 'intermediate' and 'final' outputs result from the production process. 'Final outputs' are the ultimate goals of welfare provision, such as the quality of life of clients. 'Intermediate outputs' are those which may be of interest in

Evaluation	
Research topics	*Types of information collected*
Outcomes for clients	Morale and life satisfaction Skills and behaviour problems Social contacts Engagement in activities Personal presentation Significant events
Process	Case review information Interviews with key personnel Background information
Services in practice	Physical environment Social environment Staffing
Costs	Client service receipt information Administrative costs Hospital costs

BOX 3

themselves but are essentially important only in the likelihood of their being associated with final outputs. Examples of these are the services received by clients, their physical and social environment, and the morale of staff. We aim to draw some conclusions about the relationships between the kinds of input and output in the projects. We are also particularly interested in the systems devised for the assessment of individual need and the coordination of services: the ways in which projects ascertain the views of clients and their relatives; how these can be used in conjunction with the views of the various professionals to produce the best plans for individuals, and how case managers obtain and coordinate service for clients for whom they are responsible and what are the main problems encountered in doing so.

We are using this framework as the basis for a longitudinal study. Starting in the hospitals and subsequently following the careers of clients in community services, we are in effect undertaking a series of 'before-after' comparisons of individuals, the services which they receive and the associated costs.

Our choice of instrumentation has, to some extent, been constrained by the multiplicity of requirements placed upon it. It has had to be applicable to a wide variety of people, from frail elderly people, to those with residual mental illnesses, to severely mentally handicapped people. It has also had to be transportable between 28 different project settings, brief and easy to use over large numbers of clients and yet sensitive enough to record detailed changes in particular characteristics. For a different type of task, say an in-depth study of one or two projects, we probably would have chosen differently.

The focus of our work has been largely determined by the speed at which the programme has developed and the demands it has generated. Rigorous scientific results are not yet available, although it is possible at this stage to highlight certain lessons from the pilot projects. These are based on narrative information from visits, meetings, interviews with project personnel and our twice-yearly conferences for projects.

Lessons from the pilot projects

The wide variety of types of care and models of organisation involved in the pilot project programme makes certain kinds of generalisation difficult. It also enables some general suggestions to be made over a wide range of important issues, however. Projects vary in their scale, their aims, client groups, type of service and their managerial superstructure. Geographical factors have sometimes been paramount. Different political environments may favour initiatives for particular client groups. Individual professionals, officers or politicians can be crucial catalysts.

The focus here is inevitably on problems which projects face since it is these which make the news: smooth running never makes the headlines. It is also important, though, to emphasise the successes and achievements of the care in the community programme. By January 1987, about 400 people had moved out to the community, out of a planned total of 1100. This underestimates the true progress of the programme because the numbers of people involved will accelerate in the later stages of the projects, and after their central funding ceases. Much initial work has been required to develop useful systems for referral, rehabilitation, staff and management, and to obtain and adapt buildings. Nonetheless, it can be useful to learn from others' misfortunes. There is little point in new schemes re-inventing the wheel. The following sections document some of the questions and difficulties projects have faced, which may provide lessons for the future.

Finance

The very nature of the pilot project programme has meant that many have been unable to spend money straight away. It has not been possible for slippage to be carried over beyond the three years. Demonstration projects of this kind will always need extra planning time after the funding decision has been made, in order to finalise the details and to undertake the preliminary administrative work.

Negotiation over the long-term funding of schemes has been tortuous, arising from the indefinite nature of national guidelines. The arrangements for 'dowry payments', transferred with long-stay hospital patients under resettlement schemes, vary from region to region. Some agreements have been based on average hospital costs, arbitrarily determined. Some have been agreed on the cost of new services. The need for real growth in spending for services for the priority groups has now begun to be recognised. As the Short Committee has said, genuine community care requires a real increase in resources. Who is to fill the gap if transferred funds are not sufficient?

Moving the least dependent people first may allow care in the community to start more cheaply. However, several simultaneous consequences can result from this:

— Small hospitals would be closed before large ones, because certain kinds of funds can only be recouped by closing entire institutions, so it makes economic sense to start with the smallest and therefore quickest;

— The less dependent people would be moved out, leaving the

more disabled who need the most intensive input from skilled professional staff;
— The brighter staff would read the writing on the wall and the more marketable will have their talents bought up first. They would go to the new exciting services, not necessarily where the need is greatest.

The net effect could be disastrous: for many years the most needy people would be looked after by the least talented staff in the worst institutions. Planners for hospital and community services must consider these problems and devise strategies which look beyond the immediate future.

Many pilot projects have found their original estimates to be unrealistic. More money has been needed, revenue for staffing in particular, since dependency needs have often been higher than expected. Capital costs have also escalated, due to rising house prices – especially in the southeast – and additional building works for adaptations and refurbishing.

Other areas of activity in developing services have proved unexpectedly costly. Transport costs are one example, particularly where the hospital is distant from the area of resettlement and project workers need to make frequent visits over the period of transition. Visits and outings are costly in mileage and in staff time. Transitional costs of new schemes entail not only the 'double funding' required to put a new service in place before the old one can be removed, but additional activities on top. These include administration and planning, developing staff teams and management systems, recruitment, training, acquisition of buildings, client assessment and rehabilitation training. Obtaining the full benefit entitlements for clients has not been straightforward in all cases. Schemes which rely on them for their income have run into problems if occupancy falls for any reason. Personal money is crucial for a good quality of life in the community and benefit levels can be hard for anyone to live on. The lack of incentive for clients to work, resulting from a benefit system which penalises part-time and low-wage earners, can militate against good practice.

Timescales

Nearly all projects have found that every step has taken far longer than was anticipated. This was partly because of the lottery aspect of applying for special project money, since many projects had to spend considerable time simply working out the details of their plans.

Buildings have been a major source of delay. Over-optimism about how long the search for suitable sites and premises would take; committee cycles, planning permission and fire regulations, and the builder's workers unaccountably being at another site, can make a three-year project a tiny window in the ages needed before clients have anywhere to go. Eighteen months is probably a reasonable estimate of the time taken to buy, convert, furnish and equip existing buildings for project use, and new buildings take even longer.

The care in the community projects coincided with major changes in the regulations governing residential care and nursing homes. Last-minute changes were forced in the design of community facilities; for instance, in the sizes of bedrooms. Planning permission, too, can be a minefield. The ease with which it is granted seems to vary from district council to district council all over the country. Suffice it to say that friends on the planning committee make life a lot easier. Better still, be on the committee yourself.

Fire officers, too, can be variable. The regulations themselves seem in some districts to be merely the starting point for protracted haggling. The ways in which obtrusive fire precautions can detract from a policy of normalisation are obvious: ordinary houses do not have red notices on the walls and double-thick spring-loaded doors. One also cannot help remembering that elderly people in homes are now many times as safe from fire as the average citizen. Nevertheless, it has to be acknowledged that some former hospital patients are not amongst the most careful citizens.

Many projects have ended up by making a compromise between the ideal buildings to suit their needs and those which happen to be available locally at an affordable price. This is obviously easier in areas where housing is plentiful and where the authorities involved already have resources which need to be used.

Staff recruitment has been a problem in most areas. Some authorities have been unable to appoint, or even advertise, until a series of committees has met and approved the new posts – even though the money has been available. Later, attracting qualified staff has been vexatious. New community nurses, social workers and psychologists have all been slow to materialise, and in some places appointments have simply not been made at all.

Projects should produce a management timetable from day one (to be revised as schedules alter, but to remain as a guideline), setting out what services they expect to deliver; to which clients; in which facilities; when, and, most of all, what has to be done in the intermediate stages to achieve these goals.

What does care in the community mean for hospitals?

National policy for the future of mental handicap and mental illness hospitals is far from clearcut. Staff can feel resentment and fear towards a community project which they may regard as a threat to their future livelihood, as indeed in many cases it really is. This may be exacerbated by the difference between hospital and field agency cultures, and the different models of care they may hold to.

Nurses' reactions stem from a combination of genuine concern (for example, assuming that project staff are untrained and ignorant) and the perceived threat to their own professional identity. Disbelief in the reality of the strategic plans increases the feelings of insecurity.

Psychiatrists can be a difficult group to work alongside, although some have made constructive suggestions and others have at times been leaders in the movement away from institutions. The objections some have made have been a mixture of the genuine and the defensive, exacerbated by different models of care which are employed by the different professions. Psychiatrists do hold considerable power, though, and can hold sway over major decisions such as a veto over discharges. Project staff have been refused access to wards in some cases.

Ancillary staff should not be forgotten since they are rarely included in decision-making, and are unrepresented on almost all planning bodies, although there are honourable exceptions where the unions are consulted about closures.

The backlash in favour of hospital care stimulated by relatives' groups such as Rescare should not be underestimated. In some cases they have joined forces with the unions who represent many hospital staff.

Progress in dealing with hospitals seems to be best achieved where all the relevant parties are consulted and made to feel involved at an early stage.

Pilot project staff

Many projects started out with the aim of recruiting a mixture of staff, from a variety of professional backgrounds. The different conditions of employment and career structures in different agencies have become major obstacles to progress. For example, health service staff are eligible for retirement pensions some years earlier than social services staff, and their career ladder is unsympathetic to unconventional moves. Such details have made it difficult for projects to recruit existing hospital staff – who frequently have the advantage of knowing the clients and the local context – and have sometimes led to organised refusal to cooperate with the project. Some relaxation of the rules from the centre could make life easier for community care development as a whole.

Project coordination and management are vital variables. The designation of a full- or nearly full-time coordinator at an early stage seems to be enormously helpful. It may help to involve them in finalising the project plans and liaising with other agencies, such as housing. If it is left too late, or if those who were responsible for initiation of the scheme in the first place move away, the shape of the project is liable to change markedly from its original conception. Some change is inevitable as ideas turn into reality and new people make their mark, but some continuity should be maintained where possible.

Accountability can be confusing in jointly owned schemes. Individual members of staff may find themselves torn between the project on the one hand and the mainstream (their official employer) on the other. Both are important: a project must operate in an internally consistent fashion, but it is unwise to stray too far from the parent body either. Problems can arise where local line managers may have their own ideas about the best use of an extra pair of hands.

Staff training – and in particular joint training – is something of a vexed question at the present time. Just what sort of training is most appropriate, especially for frontline care staff, is not entirely clear. The lack of a formal qualification need not imply a lack of appropriate training. Indeed, many schemes have developed their own package of training which they believe to be more useful than anything which can be bought in from elsewhere. It is worth repeating that most long-term care of dependent people has always been carried out by 'informal carers' who receive no training at all. Some training bodies now advocate a model in which all basic care is provided by unqualified people, with close support and backup from established professionals.

High levels of stress among staff are almost universal. Work in these projects seems to be particularly demanding at every level. Managers still have some client contact, but also line management of staff with whom they need to communicate frequently, budget accountability and planning, and personal responsibility for the success or otherwise of the whole venture. All of this takes place within tight financial and time constraints.

Frontline care staff who work in or manage the activities of group homes, for instance, are also subject to much stress and anxiety. Relatively junior staff, who might previously have worked within the protective umbrella of a large institution, are suddenly in sole charge of a group of residents. Shift patterns can mean long and inconvenient hours, often in very intensive contact with the people they are taking care of. Some projects have experienced an excessively high turnover of frontline staff, probably as a direct consequence of the stressful work pattern, especially where backup and support are not well organised.

Turnover has also been a feature of management staff, although for different reasons. In the final stages of several first-round projects, many of the people in key management posts have moved on to other jobs. Nobody would criticise those individuals for sensibly planning their own careers. The damage, however limited, which must ensue when projects fail to keep such people should perhaps be cause for concern. Some may find it hard to maintain their initial momentum and others can change direction entirely.

Multidisciplinary working brings many advantages, such as the pooling of different skills and perspectives. On the other side of the coin, establishment of an effective team is never easy, and mistrust between the professions does not disappear overnight. Most disciplines, at some level or other, continue to harbour insecurities about the exclusiveness of their particular skills and the niche which they occupy. Teams may find it necessary to delineate some duties very clearly so that each profession retains an area which is unique to them, whilst allowing other activities to be shared between members more or less equally.

The local context

Access to resources can be difficult where projects are isolated, and even fundamental services such as day care and medical attention have not always been forthcoming. Even large projects which provide many services themselves will need to call on outside professional help occasionally or make use of, say, local education facilities.

Nor will too much segregation help when clients want to mix with local people. A specialist service run entirely for people from hospital will continue to be seen as separate unless efforts are made to share some activities or facilities with people who already live in the area.

Tapping into the primary health care services has not always been straightforward. Many GPs appear reluctant to take people they view as 'high risk' onto their panels. As the community care movement grows, it may be necessary for some encouragement to be given to GPs to accept responsibility for people with special needs, perhaps through family practitioner committees.

Public relations, with the local community in particular, continue to be a difficult area. There is no simple formula to guide a project in its approach to the neighbours, but personal contact or silence seems to be preferred to a 'high profile' announcement. This is consistent with maintaining the greatest possible degree of respect for the individual clients concerned.

Further education of the general public about people who have mental illness, mental handicaps or problems associated with ageing is still needed. This will have to be approached on many fronts simultaneously if attitudes and understanding are to improve, as they must, before it is too late.

Matters of practice

The much debated notion of 'normalisation' is in the forefront of almost all community care developments, although probably misunderstood by many. The messengers of the normalisation creed themselves advise that it should not be written as a set of rules 'on tablets of stone', but rather used as a value base from which certain general principles emerge naturally. The fundamental notion is the full appreciation and valuation of all people as essentially human, instead of labelling some as a race apart, by virtue of handicap or other special characteristics. From this follow the rights of all to human dignity, choices, privacy where desired and services designed to fit one's individual configuration of needs. The philosophy has undoubtedly had a tremendous impact in the last few years on our perception of the services we provide for people and the ideals toward which they should aim.

There are dangers too, particularly where partial or incorrect understanding of the principles might encourage inflexible solutions or, worse, the acceptance of poor standards of living because 'normal' people have to endure them (such as resettlement in deprived inner city housing estates where no-one is valued).

Normalisation can influence all aspects of service delivery. Debate over the degree of risk or safety that should be allowed is one example; how far to encourage someone to dress acceptably or fashionably is another.

The inclusion of a rehabilitation stage in the resettlement programme is another point on which opinions differ. Should all training (in daily living skills, dealing with people outside, etc) take place in one's own home, once resettled – and thus minimise the number of disruptive moves – or does it make moving easier to take it in small steps at a time? Probably, as ever, different solutions suit different people.

How to replace the 'community' of a hospital should be a question of concern to planners. That community provides a sense of 'belongingness', of having a position and a role, greeting familiar faces as you walk around the grounds, dropping in to the social club or another ward for a chat and, perhaps, helping to deliver the post or the laundry. It will not be easy to replace all of this, though most of us manage to develop networks which are meaningful to us in different ways, which do not necessarily depend on immediate proximity to home. Perhaps the notion of 'asylum' should be raised at this point – whether it really describes a place or more a state of mind, and whether a crowded hospital is actually the best place to provide it?

Relatives are also important and should be encouraged to participate wherever possible, even though there can sometimes be conflicts of interest. Where they want to be involved, it may be helpful to arrange meetings at times which suit them and in places which are easily accessible.

Citizen advocacy will also probably grow in importance as a means to safeguard the rights of vulnerable individuals and as a vital link with the community in its true sense.

A partially objective commentator (such as a locally based researcher) has proved to be valuable in some schemes. Such a person may be able to observe features (and problems) which are invisible to staff who are deeply involved in its day to day operations. Feedback and discussion may help to unstick some seemingly insoluble problems, indicate new directions for development or simply act as a sounding board to improve the understanding of what is happening in the project.

Pilot projects and their status

Demonstration programmes of this kind can, and perhaps should, be used to prepare the way for major policy changes, by experimentation with methods and gauging their relative usefulness in advance. During the pilot period of care in the community, policy events have caught up with and, to an extent, taken over the trail they were to blaze. Most localities already have strategic plans for community services for the priority groups at varying stages of development.

Many of the projects, nevertheless, have gone further down the community care road than the 'mainstream' services which surround them. Useful lessons are emerging, particularly in specific methods and techniques of operation even though the results of a full evaluation may appear too late for some authorities. The large projects, in particular, are exploring new strategies for the management and delivery of community services on a scale which has never before been attempted.

A major change in the nature of services to be delivered, as embodied in the care in the community programme, must therefore imply that the huge agencies involved should adapt to the new situation. Inevitable though this is, it will also be gradual. A conflict already exists, and may well grow, between creative marginal intervention and incremental adaptation of large organisations. The projects themselves might most usefully merge into the mainstream, thus contributing to an incremental change. On the other hand, some will probably remain on the fringes as something of an oddity, continually reminding the main authorities of the alternatives which are possible.

Special projects, and changes of direction, need both impetus from the grassroots, and commitment and authority from above if they are to succeed. Maintaining that impetus may be a challenge in the years to come; special projects and new ideas can stimulate enthusiasm at all levels, but the real questions about success must be asked once the novelty has worn off.

Notes

1   DHSS (1981a), *Care in the Community: A Consultative Document*, London, HMSO.
2   DHSS (1983a), *Care in the Community*, HC(83)6, LAC(83)5, London, HMSO.
3   Davies, B and Knapp, M (1981), *Old People's Homes and the Production of Welfare*, London, Routledge Kegan Paul.

Conclusion

Dick Stockford

Conclusions are hard to draw from the previous chapters. This is in spite of the fact that all authors have tried to present an honest appraisal – albeit from different perspectives – of their efforts to integrate care provision. Each of the authors has drawn attention to those areas where they feel improvements can be made and to direct the practitioner through a series of hints and prospects for the future. But the reasons their conclusions are hard to deduce must be linked to the subject itself. There remain some substantial ambiguities. These ambiguities appear in the arenas of evaluation (what is generally recognised as a 'good' project?) and of power (who are good projects designed for?) These two issues are discussed prior to an examination, within the context of these unresolved ambiguities, of those factors which would appear to be linked with success.

'Good' joint projects

There is no commonly recognised good joint project. In much the same way that social workers refer to 'good enough' parenting we must now recognise 'good enough' integration. Different perspectives will affect this judgement: perspectives associated with the position that the evaluator takes and, of course, the expectations that the evaluator has of the project. As we have seen, politicians do have high expectations and subsequently experience frustration at the inability of their practitioners to translate a political commitment into practice. Practitioners, on the other hand, may be relieved (if not satisfied) to have established a process through which this integration can be mediated: not the end product, nor the service delivered but the juggernaut levered, cajoled and persuaded onto a reasonable track.

But both practitioners and politicians – whatever their expectations and however they are satisfied – have at least made their expectations clear; consumers have not. In Cockburn's terms consumers are the serviced, politicians and practitioners are the servicers and represent all the power of the corporate state, or in our terms, those who are integrating provision have power, those who are benefiting have not. Most providers would fully accept that they know little of what their customers actually want, and service planners struggling for the stability of the system are often not in a position to provide any insight, on a systematic basis, to customer requirements. In fact, customers would have to vote with their feet before a problem was identified.

So there is an uneasy and unpalatable possibility which remains untested: that given free choice the customers may not want their services integrated, and that even if they did, they may not want them in the particular forms that they are being provided. And just in case this argument appears abstract and irrelevant, we need only to refer to the latest report of the Audit Commission on care in the community, which has commended the 'parceling up' of mentally ill clients (who would in future become the responsibility of the NHS) and mentally handicapped clients (to become the responsibility of social services departments). Whether any mentally handicapped or ill customers have expressed an opinion as to the virtue of these options is not mentioned and certainly not cited in evidence. What would be the likely reaction if it were proposed that black people were, in future, to become 'the responsibility' of the National Health Service and white people the social services departments'? Of course these proposals are not examples of integration – quite the opposite. It appears that we assume the good of integration to our customers because we do assume their powerlessness; because we expect that in the normal run of things we all act in an integrated way, we make the agencies link up to meet needs and this requires power. Those who lack power and are not able to demand the links require our determination to provide it. This does not seem an unreasonable position in itself – many services grew from charitable organisations with one such objective – what does jar with a certain awkwardness, a generation after Seebohm, is that still no-one bothers to check out our reasonableness with our customers! So perhaps one resolution that the next generation of planners should have is that another two decades must not slip by without our developing a proper and reasonable relationship with our customers, be they clients, patients, tenants or just people.

But none of this should halt the noble enterprise. We can be reasonably sure that we are improving on past provision and attitudes from one important piece of evidence. Since the development of the workhouses the evolution of accommodation for elderly people has been largely by local authority housing departments who have made sheltered accommodation available to elderly people unable, or unwilling, to live in their own homes; local authority social services departments have provided varying amounts and quality of residential care for those unable to live alone, or with others, and the NHS has provided (less so now than previously) long stay 'chronic' provision for elderly people usually in back wards in large institutions. And what has been the cry of the elderly person since the development of the workhouse? 'I want to stay in my own home, or at least a home of my own, that is where I want to live and die'. Carers may be relieved when Mum enters an old people's home or a geriatric hospital, but how does Mum feel? We do know that Mum becomes more, not less, dependent, more, not less, institutionalised, and separated from her community and her past.

But these services have been developed as separate strands by different organisations, each with clearly defined criteria and each responding to a specific legislative requirement to meet a particular need. Unfortunately none have been given the remit to listen to what Mum wants – a home of her own, and services provided in that home.

So if we could be more sensible to the expectations of our customers, and if we can assume that this is at least the direction in which they would wish to move, how can we ensure that we get there as quickly, competently and efficiently as possible? What aspects of the provision require attention if the enterprise is to optimise its chances of success?

Criteria for success

Success would appear to be closely correlated to projects where:

Philosophy and values are congruent rather than diverse

It is of course difficult to assess the philosophy of an organisation, or for that matter the individuals who represent it. This means that success will be dependent upon a fairly non-systematic assessment, but this may not be as infeasible as it sounds. In Cambridgeshire the development of joint statements of intent between authorities has been an attempt to tease out at both practitioner and political level the values underlying joint provision and make them explicit. Likewise, the Delphi experiment discussed here represents a highly systematic and iterative process aimed at reaching a common view on integration. It is easy to assume that common philosophy leads to a common purpose – not always, but the effect of the lack of it has been demonstrated in this book in relation to the integration of both large highly formal structures or small informal organisations.

Values are based on normalisation for the consumer

The continued emphasis of this book on values is not accidental. It is not accidental, partly because the authors believe that they need to be more strongly held and stated, and partly because they believe that without a commitment to these values there is a real danger that a focus on process will overtake the focus on the customer. The effort involved in establishing a joint planning system that works is considerable; without a clearer understanding as to why it should exist there is a danger that it will have an end in itself. No one has bettered normalisation as a value. Its strength is that it reasserts the status of the customer as a peer making a fundamental demand on the planner and practitioner to be enabled to live in and as part of a wider society.

Process thrives but does not dominate

Process, like a machine, can draw gasps of delight, but just like a machine it is prone to breakdown and at the end is not a good self-regulator. Process benefits a jointly planned project by providing a clear framework for timescales, authorisation, agreement and funding of the enterprise. In short, it helps to avoid simple pitfalls. And process does considerably simplify the evaluation and in so doing enables, most importantly of all, lessons to be learned. Because of these important benefits it is easy to see why process can often dominate. Indeed, much of the advice to health and local authorities on the establishment of joint planning systems in the 1970s and 80s has focused much more heavily on process than on outcome. It is a necessary but not sufficient aspect of the good project.

An entrepreneur is managing the process

It is easy to assume, where plans are well developed and projects delivered to a clear timetable, that these are being achieved by a powerful process. It almost certainly isn't – however graceful the liftoff of Concorde or the silky smooth acceleration of a Rolls Royce, a great deal of sweat and oily rags have gone into achieving this effect. The importance of the engineer is too often ignored. Engineers in this context are sometimes referred to as entrepreneurs, reticulists, networkers or brokers, but they exist in all successful projects. They are often the guardians of the value system, the embodiment of the philosophy, the scourge of committee secretaries, and they see it as their responsibility to deliver the service. In spite of their importance in delivering projects, few formal references are made to these individuals in evaluation reports, and fewer in instructions on process, but it is they who invariably ensure that process only dominates when necessary. Good engineers will know their machines intimately, but so too will they understand the prevailing conditions and the strengths of the staff working for them. They will do all they can to adjust, tweak or, if necessary, modify a machine in order to achieve their objective.

The need to control and the need to cooperate are not competing forces

Both cannot be achieved at the same time and insistence on the former will emasculate the latter. This is not a plea that participating agencies have to 'roll on their backs' – far from it, but they equally cannot insist on colonising another's territory. Each has to play to the other's strength. This requires careful negotiation and, if possible, joint training, but it does demand a recognition of strengths rather than a concentration on weaknesses. This often leads to a better fit of services than any merger might achieve.

Increasingly it is argued that control must be wrested from the service providers and given to the customers if real choice is to be exercised and controlled so as to be productive to the development of acceptable services. This is developed to some extent through the expansion of funding for residential care for elderly people through the social security system. Even so the need to regulate, monitor and control the supply of these services has, sadly, been all too often brought to public attention. It is clear that the provision of choice in this context may only represent the power to choose between the poor and the mediocre.

Resources are assumed to be better used rather than saved

Few people now believe that community care is a cheap option; unfortunately many seem to act as if it was. It is extraordinary that a movement towards community care could have been built on the assumption that the massive economies of scale achieved by poorly staffed, large wards in ancient institutions could possibly finance individually planned, around the clock provision, in small homes in the community. Nonetheless, this would appear to be the case and perhaps not surprisingly there has been much disappointment generated amongst politicians about the high cost of community care services on the one hand, and the scandalous understimulation and exploitation of the seaside boarding houses on the other. This problem of perception appears to have been brought about partly by the over-enthusiasm and exaggerated claims of the practitioners promoting community based care, and partly (probably mostly) by some rather naive 'back of the envelope' calculations.

Integrating care can make no assumption of cost savings. In fact it may result in a clearer statement of need and, therefore, an exposure of service gaps. Certainly, schemes which have assumed such savings do not seem to have produced good or lasting outcomes and are of little long-term benefit to customers.

Political will exists to integrate provision

In this context political will relates to the non-officer or elected members of the agencies attempting integration. It needs to be stressed both that without this will integration will fail, and that such will can be established and developed since it does not necessarily exist in abundance naturally. The reason for this lack of natural will is not hard to find when the separate development of caring services is recalled. So much time has been spent repelling boarders that the instinct to attack is usually greater than the will to cooperate. But this can be altered, and one of the first moves of the skilled entrepreneur will be to bring together opinion leaders amongst politicians in order to develop a commitment to integration. This commitment can only be developed in the context of the precursors for success already mentioned – such a process is not easy but it is vital to the good project.

To select one of these contributions to success as of highest priority would be invidious. Integrating care provision, by its very nature, depends on the skilful and sensitive blending of each of them. At the centre must always lie a powerful commitment to the care of people and a determination to make things work, sometimes against considerable odds and often in conditions which are not ideal. To the resolute entrepreneur committed to this form of alchemy, I can do no better than offer Mark Twain's advice:

> When angry, count to a hundred; when very angry, swear.

References

Audit Commission (1986) *Making a reality of community care*, London, HMSO.
Cockburn, C (1977) *The Local State*, London, Pluto Press.

Notes on authors

Rob Ballantyne

Rob Ballantyne is Director of Planning and Information for Southern Derbyshire Health Authority. Before that he was Head of Research and Planning for Hereford and Worcester Social Services Department.

Malcolm Cooper

Malcolm Cooper graduated as a botanist and was a parish priest for eight years before entering local government as a housing officer. For the past five years he has been Housing and Environmental Services Manager at East Cambridgeshire District Council and is Principal Housing Adviser to the Association of District Councils.

Brian Gale

Brian Gale is currently Planning Processes Officer with the Corporate Policy and Planning Department of Cambridgeshire County Council. He is a graduate in both Economics and Rural and Regional Resources Planning, and previously worked as an economist, transport planner and land use planner.

Gill Garton

Gill Garton has worked in Priority Services planning with North East Thames Regional Health Authority and as a policy researcher in Cambridgeshire's Corporate Planning Section. She is currently responsible for community health services planning in Cambridge District Health Authority.

Nick Miller

Nick Miller is Principal Research Officer, Norfolk County Council Social Services Department. Previously he worked in an inner London borough Social Services Department in research and planning roles.

Robert Nisbet

After graduating, Robert undertook several social work positions in residential and fieldwork. Following professional training he worked for a number of small voluntary organisations, including a spell as Project Manager for Charnwood Mencap Society. He is currently an Acting Principal Personnel Officer with Nottinghamshire Social Services Department.

Greg Parston

Greg Parston is Director of Field Development programmes at the King's Fund College. Prior to joining the College, he was a Chief Officer on the management board of Downstate Medical Centre in New York and Assistant Professor in health policy management at New York University. He has held posts in several countries, including Director of Regional Health Services Planning Programmes in Canada and Australia and Public Service Resident with the US National Science Foundation.

Judy Renshaw

Judy Renshaw has recently become Director of Good Practices in Mental Health but immediately before this worked with her co-author monitoring and evaluating the government's care in the community initiative. She is a psychologist and qualified social worker who has both research and practice experience.

Dick Stockford

Dick Stockford is Deputy Director of Social Services (Head of Operations) for Cambridgeshire. He has been involved in research and planning of the social services since 1970, both in universities and local authorities. He has published, with others, *Social Work in Context* in 1983, which compared social services provision in urban and rural areas.

Corinne Thomason

Corinne Thomason is a Research Fellow at the Personal Social Services Research Unit at Kent University and has been involved with the community care initiative for three years. She came to academic research from a practice background in local authority and health service management. Her particular sphere of interest is the mixed economy of welfare in service provision.

Andrew Webster

Andrew Webster has worked as a policy researcher in Cambridge-shire's Corporate Planning Section, as Assistant Service Co-ordinator with Oxford Regional Health Authority, and is currently Joint Care Planning Officer for Cambridgeshire Social Services.

Michael White

Michael White worked for the Ford Motor Company before training as a town planner. He has been a researcher, planner and developer in social services and is now Assistant Director (Planning and Development) for Lincolnshire.

Simon Whitehead

Currently works as Assistant Director of Social Services for Suffolk County Council. He has worked previously in development and planning in Derbyshire and began his career as a social worker employed in both Westminster and Berkshire.

Peter Whittingham

After graduating in the Natural Sciences, Peter Whittingham became a local authority and subsequently a university researcher at Bath. A book entitled *Joint Approaches to Social Policy* (1988) written with the research team, is about to be published. He has managed a personal social services unit concerned with planning, training, community development, and welfare benefits and is now Assistant Director (Planning and Development) for Social Services in North Yorkshire.

Gerald Wistow

Gerald Wistow was the founding Deputy Director of the Centre for Research in Social Policy at Loughborough University and is now its Co-Director. He has written widely on these issues and his most recent book (with David Hunter) is *Community Care in Britain: Variations on a Theme*, 1987. Gerald Wistow has acted as an adviser to parliamentary, governmental and other national bodies and is a member of the National Council for Voluntary Organisations' working group on joint planning.

Index